D1295570

Nancy Hanks

Kentucky Girl

Illustrated by Gray Morrow

Nancy Hanks

Kentucky Girl

By Augusta Stevenson

THE **BOBBS-MERRILL** COMPANY, INC.
A SUBSIDIARY OF HOWARD W. SAMS & CO., INC.
Publishers • INDIANAPOLIS • NEW YORK

To the Pioneer Society of Indiana

In commemoration of that immortal pioneer family—Nancy, Thomas, and Abraham Lincoln.

For this story of the childhood of Abraham Lincoln's mother I have chosen to follow in a general way the basic account given of her in Nancy Hanks Lincoln: A Frontier Portrait, *by Harold E. Briggs and Ernestine B. Briggs (Bookman Associates, New York, 1952). I acknowledge warm thanks for their satisfying research.*

Illustrations

Full pages

Numerous smaller illustrations

Contents

CHILDHOOD OF FAMOUS AMERICANS ®

★ ★ ★

Books by Augusta Stevenson

★ Nancy Hanks

Kentucky Girl

The Dangerous Journey

Young Nancy Hanks had just gone to sleep. So now her mother had a chance to talk with her own sister.

"Rachel, I'm worried about Nancy," she began. "The child seems to be frightened about something. She won't let me leave her. She cries if I'm out of the room."

"I've noticed that," Mrs. Berry replied, "but I'm not surprised, Lucy. She has gone through a good deal for a four-year-old. Her father's death not long ago——"

"She can't understand that," Lucy Hanks interrupted. "She keeps on looking for him."

11

"I suppose she can't understand why she was brought here and why she isn't in her own home, either," said Rachel.

"She can't," Lucy said. "I've tried to explain to her. I've told her that I couldn't run the farm by myself."

"Of course you couldn't. It isn't easy to farm in this part of Virginia. The land is too poor," Rachel answered.

"My husband never had good crops."

"Then how could you if James couldn't? I'm glad you consented to live with us."

"You and Richard have been very good to me," Lucy said.

"We should be. You're my youngest sister and I love you dearly—and you know I love Nancy. She's such a pretty child with her dark hair and dark eyes. She's sweet, too, and gentle."

"Her Uncle Richard seems to like her."

"Indeed he does! So do our sons."

12

"I was afraid the boys wouldn't want a girl around. They're older."

"That's true, they are. Frank is ten, and Ned will be eight this fall. But they would be glad to play with Nancy if she'd let them."

"She will as soon as she gets used to them."

However, Nancy didn't get used to her boy cousins. She wouldn't play with them, and she wouldn't leave her mother. Everything was so strange in her new home. There were so many people coming and going all the time.

"You needn't be afraid of them," her mother said. "Some of them are relatives and others are neighbors."

The little girl couldn't explain her fear. She didn't know it was their talk that frightened her. They all said they wanted to move away, to a new country, and Uncle Richard said he would go with them.

Then one day Nancy heard her mother say

she was going, too. Now the child was terrified.
Her father had gone away and hadn't come back.
She thought her mother and the others were go-
ing to leave her, too.

So she followed Mrs. Hanks all day long. She
clung to her mother's dress if anyone tried to
take her outside. No one scolded her. Everyone
knew there was fear in her childish mind.

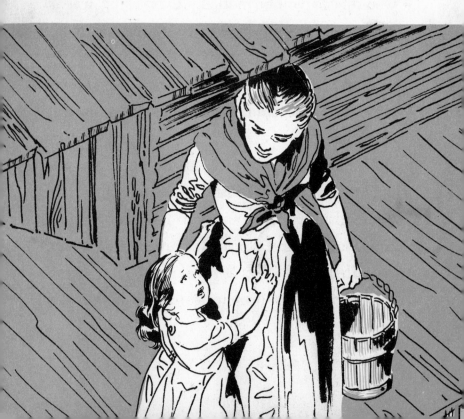

Mrs. Hanks had to be firm the day she and the other women made soap for the journey. "You can't be with me this morning, Nancy," she said. "There will be two fires and two kettles of boiling soap. It won't be safe for you out there. You might get too close to the fires."

"I'll keep her away," said Frank.

"I'll help," said Ned.

"I'll need you boys to shuck corn," said their father. "It's time we got our corn meal ready for the journey."

Presently they were all gone and Nancy was alone in the cabin. She couldn't get out because the door was fastened outside. She couldn't even look out the one window. The hole was covered with thick greased paper.

She could hear her aunt and mother talking, however, and she listened until she went to sleep. When she woke up the talking had stopped. There wasn't a sound anywhere.

Nancy was terrified. "They've gone!" she thought. "They've moved away! They forgot to take me with them!"

Then she screamed and screamed. Her mother and aunt came running. They were trying to quiet her when Mr. Berry came with the boys.

"What's the matter?" he asked. "We heard her screaming, Rachel."

"She's frightened about our moving away," Rachel said. "See if you can make her understand why we're going, Richard."

Mr. Berry took Nancy on his lap and spoke gently. "You like corn-meal johnnycakes and corn pone mush, don't you?"

The little girl nodded. Then her uncle went on: "Well, Nancy, we can't have any of those good things to eat if we stay in Virginia. I can't raise enough corn for our meal. The land here is worn out."

"Like an old dress," her mother added.

16

"So we're going to a new country where the soil is rich. Corn grows tall there in Kentucky. I'll raise big crops and we'll have all the corn meal we can use."

Nancy was still troubled. "Am I going with you, Mother?" she asked.

"Of course you are! You'll ride in a basket tied to my saddle. All the young children will ride that way."

"You'll have fun," said Frank. "I wish I could get my legs in a basket."

"So do I," said Ned.

Nancy jumped down from her uncle's lap and ran to her mother. "I won't cry any more," she said. "I want to ride in a basket."

FOOD—BULLETS—BABIES

Nancy wasn't afraid to leave her mother now that she knew she would not be left behind. She

played with her cousins when they had time. Today she watched them work. They were hanging strips of raw meat on a high pole.

"The sun will dry it," Frank explained. "We'll take it with us on the journey and it won't spoil the way raw meat would."

That afternoon she heard her uncle and some neighbors plan for the long trip.

"We must take enough meal for thirty-two persons," said her uncle. "We'll eat corn bread three times a day."

"There's plenty of game in the forest," said another. "We'll get our fresh meat as we go."

"We'll need plenty of bullets to shoot the game," added a third man. "Every man must mold his own."

"We'll need an extra supply in case of an Indian attack, too," added Richard Berry. He could say this now because Nancy had gone.

"That's true," said the third man. "The Indians

have killed a good many settlers who were on their way to Kentucky."

"They don't want white men there working farms. They don't live there themselves. They keep the land for their hunting ground."

"We can drive off a large band. We'll have enough men and boys with guns."

In the cabin Mrs. Berry and her sister Lucy were getting dinner. Two of Nancy's aunts were getting their babies ready for the journey.

Each woman held her baby on her lap. Every time one cried, the mother placed her hand over its mouth. She held it there till the baby's face grew red.

"Mother! Look at the babies!" cried Nancy. "They're choking!"

"Your aunts won't let them choke. They are teaching them not to cry."

"We shut off their breath for a moment," one aunt explained. "It hurts them a little and they don't like it. So they soon learn not to cry. They mustn't cry."

"That's the way Indian mothers train their babies," said the other aunt. "They don't dare to let them cry on the trail. It would tell their enemies where they were."

"If our babies cry the Indians will know where we are," added the other lady.

"Indians!" exclaimed Nancy.

"We haven't told her about them," Mrs. Hanks explained. "Still, she has to know about them before we start."

"I'm afraid of Indians, Mother."

"We won't even see them if we're quiet."

At last the food, bullets, and babies were ready. In the spring of 1788 the Berrys, their relatives, and neighbors set out for Kentucky. They couldn't use wagons because there were no roads.

Only a narrow trail led to the mountains and

over them. So this was the path they used. Everyone walked except the women with young children. They rode horses and carried their babies.

Men with guns were always on guard. So were the older boys who drove the pack horses. These boys were armed, too, and they guarded the older girls who drove the cows.

Many young children rode in baskets tied to their mothers' saddles. Little Nancy Hanks in her basket waved and smiled at her young cousins in theirs. They waved and smiled at her. It was fun for all of them—at first.

After a while Nancy began to worry because she couldn't see her Uncle Richard.

"He's one of the scouts," her mother explained. "He has to go on ahead of the rest to look out for Indians."

Before long the little girl had another worry. Her legs began to hurt and she wanted to get out of her basket.

"I can't stop now, Nancy. I have to wait till our leader orders a halt. Look at the pretty flowers along the trail. You'll forget your legs."

Nancy looked at the flowers, but she couldn't forget her legs. They hurt so bad she wanted to cry, but she didn't. She remembered the babies—they hadn't cried yet.

Other little legs were cramped also, but not a child cried. They were glad, though, to be lifted from their baskets at rest stops, and they were glad to walk about and run.

They played around the big campfire every night for a little while. Then they were put to bed on a blanket spread over a pile of dry leaves. Another blanket covered them.

Nancy slept by her mother's side. Mrs. Lucy Hanks held her daughter close when wolves howled and panthers screamed in the forest about them.

"They can't hurt us, dear," she would whisper.

"Don't be frightened. Your Uncle Richard is guarding the camp."

WILL INDIANS FIND THEM?

When the settlers reached the Cumberland Mountains they had to be very careful. This was Indian country. The children were told to speak softly. No fires were lighted, and no one was allowed to shoot a gun.

They ate their dried meat now and corn bread. Cows were milked every day, so young children had milk to drink.

The trail grew steeper as they climbed the mountains. Mrs. Hanks walked and led the horse. Nancy couldn't talk to her mother now and she was lonely.

This was when she began to watch birds and listen to their calls. Redbirds, blue jays, woodpeckers, blackbirds and yellow birds flitted

about. They were building their nests and sing-
ing and whistling.

Nancy loved it. She was never lonely now.
She tried to make bird calls herself, but always
softly so Indians wouldn't hear.

One day the noontime stop was over and the
long line was almost ready to move. Women
were lifting their children into the baskets. Mrs.
Hanks looked about for Nancy, but she couldn't
find her. No one knew where she was.

Then Frank Berry remembered something.
"I saw her watching a redbird. Maybe she followed it into the forest, Aunt Lucy."

"But I told her not to leave the trail! I told
her Indians might be out there."

"Maybe she forgot. She was trying to whistle
like the bird. It was funny—I had to laugh."

Now the leader came to see what was wrong.
"We'll look for Nancy," he said. "You women
stay here and watch the children."

The men went into the forest at once. They called Nancy softly, but there was no answer.

"We've gone as far as a four-year-old child could walk," said the leader at last. "I fear she's been captured by Indians. We'll look for moccasin prints and follow them."

Back in camp the women waited. They knew the men had been gone too long. Finally Mrs. Hanks began to weep. She was sure Nancy had been seized.

Her sister and the others tried to comfort her. "Don't give up," they said. "You'll hear good news when the men come."

They didn't believe their own words, however. They all thought that Nancy had been captured by the Indians.

At last the men came, and Nancy with with them! Her Uncle Richard carried her but she didn't know it, for she was sound asleep.

"We found her under a tree," he said. "A redbird was on a branch above. Its whistling led us to her. Frank gave us that idea."

He put Nancy in her basket without waking her. Then the long line moved at once. On and on they followed their leader.

Day after day and week after week the settlers traveled, through rain and cold and heat. At last they reached the country called Kentucky. Even then they couldn't stop until they came to a fort, but only their leader knew where it was. So once again the settlers followed him through rain and cold and heat.

They crossed rivers. They forded creeks. They climbed hills. They went through valleys.

By now the women were tired out and the children were miserable. Little Nancy no longer waved to other children in baskets, and they no longer waved to her. They couldn't even smile. They were too tired to smile any more.

Then one day the settlers came to a clearing

in the forest. And there in the center of the clearing stood the fort! The high stockade around it was a beautiful sight to the weary travelers, for it meant safety at last.

The gate was opened for them and they hurried through it into the fort. Now they were safe in the lovely land of Kentucky.

Signals and
Moccasin Prints

IT WAS early morning in 1791 when Ned Berry saw the runaway horses and wagon. He was eleven now and knew the danger. The horses were tearing down the narrow rough road. And the wagon seemed about to tip over.

"If it does, the people in it will be hurt," he thought. But he couldn't stop a team by himself so he ran to the barn for help. He knew the Negro worker Luke would be there, and maybe his father and brother Frank.

"Quick, a runaway wagon!" he shouted when he reached the barn door. "There were people in the wagon, too!"

"Come along, all of you!" his father shouted. Then he ran from the barn.

Frank and Ned followed him, and Luke followed them.

Mrs. Berry rushed from the cabin to see what was going on.

Before any of them reached the road a strange thing happened. The wagon was driven into the yard. The horses were stopped and the driver jumped to the ground with his gun.

"Indians!" he cried. "Jump down, Sally! Quick! They might have followed us."

The young woman on the driver's seat jumped to the ground. She was pale with fright.

"We heard their signals," the man went on. "They were trying to surround us."

"Did you see them?" Mr. Berry asked.

"I didn't need to. I heard their signals."

"So did I," said the woman. "An owl hooted twice near by."

30

"And owls don't hoot in daytime," the man added. "I haven't lived on the frontier long, but I know that."

"They might if some noise woke them up," said Mr. Berry. "In fact I've heard them during the day."

"It wasn't an owl," the man declared firmly.

"We haven't seen any Indians for some time, sir. They sold all their land on this side of the mountains to white men. They promised to stay on the other side."

"They won't keep their promise. They'll come out of the mountains again and they'll kill settlers and burn cabins. They'll steal cattle and horses just as they used to do. We heard all about it."

"It scared me," said the woman. "I'm afraid to live in the Kentucky woods. We're going back to a settlement."

"Hoo-oo! Hoo-oo!"

"There's the signal again!" the man exclaimed. "It's closer! Get your gun, sir!"

Just then a young girl came from the orchard.

"There's your Indian!" Mr. Berry said with a smile. "She's the one who hooted. Nancy! Come here!" he called.

"But she's too young!" the lady cried.

"She's past seven," Mrs. Berry replied.

"She fools me all the time," said Ned. "I'll hear a pigeon cooing and I'll go out to catch it, but there isn't any pigeon. It's Nancy."

"She can imitate almost any bird," said Frank, now thirteen.

"She's my niece, Nancy Hanks," Mrs. Berry explained. "She lives with us."

"I hope the Indians didn't kill her parents," said the man.

"No, her father died. Then her mother married again after she came to Kentucky. She lives in the next county."

"I'd think she'd want Nancy with her," said the lady.

"She did and so did her husband, Henry Sparrow, but his farm was away off in the forest. There was no settlement near and no fort. They knew Nancy would be safer here with us. Besides, we wanted her."

"Our children were all boys," Mr. Berry put in. "Two of them are married."

"You said safer, Mrs. Berry. Did you mean from Indians?"

"Yes, sir. They were always prowling about at that time. It wasn't safe for a child to play outside the cabin where the Sparrows live."

"There are more people here in Washington County," Mr. Berry explained. "The Beechland settlement is near and so is our fort. Indians have never bothered us much."

"I don't blame your sister for putting her daughter in a safer place," said the lady.

"She's like our daughter now," said Mrs. Berry. "We love her dearly."

"I should think you would. She has a lovely face," said the lady.

Nancy reached the wagon now and her uncle spoke to her at once. "Were you hooting in the orchard just now?"

"Yes, Uncle Richard. I hoped an owl would answer, but it didn't."

"Well, you gave us a scare," said the settler. "We thought you were a band of Indians. Now climb up, Sally, we must be getting on."

Presently the man and his wife were gone. Then Nancy imitated a turtle dove. "That's to tell them good-by," she said.

"It's an Indian signal, too," said her aunt. "You'd better stop that, Nancy. They'll get scared again and come back."

"Would this be better? Whip-poor-will! Whip-poor-will!" Nancy called softly.

"You've learned a lot of things here in Kentucky, Miss Nancy," said Luke.

"Of course! I'm a Kentucky girl."

"Hooray!" cried her cousins.

Then everyone went back to work.

"GO TO THE FORT! HURRY!"

Sometimes relatives came to visit the Berry family. They always told Nancy she was a lucky little girl. "You have a nice home here," they said. "It's one of the largest cabins in the county. In fact, it's a double cabin, and you have a little room of your own in the loft."

Today her Aunt Sarah was saying even more. "It's a beautiful spot. The cabin is surrounded by beech trees. You can see the Beech River from the front gate."

"I think it's pretty. Mother likes it, too. She likes to come here," Nancy said.

"It's lovely! No wonder they named this part of the country Beechland. Your Uncle Richard was smart to settle here."

"He said it was a good place to raise horses."

"The best in the United States," Aunt Sarah said. "But he's always busy clearing land for new fields."

"He has to raise more feed all the time," said Nancy. "That's because he has more horses and colts every year."

"It takes hard work to clear land. Chopping down great forest trees isn't easy."

"Luke and Frank help. Ned does a lot of work, too. He chops off small branches."

"Everyone works in the wilderness, Nancy. We have to, to stay alive."

"I help Aunt Rachel keep the cabin clean."

"I know you do," said Aunt Sarah. "Rachel said she couldn't get along without you."

Nancy had outside chores also. She hunted

hens' nests and gathered eggs. She brought vegetables from the garden. She carried fruit from the orchard. She picked wild strawberries, blackberries, and gooseberries.

She watched for wild grapes and crab apples to ripen. She tried to get them before the crows did. Sometimes she got them first. Sometimes the crows got them first.

"There wasn't a grape left on the vines," she complained one day at dinner. "You should have heard those crows laughing at me."

"Laughing!" exclaimed Ned. "Nancy, crows can't laugh at you."

"Well, I guess I just imagined it, then," Nancy said. "But it sounded like laughing."

She went to the big spring for water three or four times every day. It was at the foot of a little hill below the cabin near the road. Back of it was the dense wood.

This morning Nancy saw a good deal of mud

37

around the spring. So she took off her shoes and put them on a log near by.

As she went closer she saw footprints in the mud. The prints had been made by moccasins, and they were fresh, too!

"Everyone on the farm wears shoes," Nancy thought. She was frightened now. She was certain she knew who had made those prints—Indians! "They're hiding here—they're watching me now," she thought.

Nancy didn't show her fear. She filled her bucket at the spring. She put on her shoes, but her hands trembled as she fastened them.

She made herself climb the hill slowly with her bucket. When she reached the top she knew the Indians couldn't see her, so she ran. The water was spilled, but this didn't matter now.

"Indians!" she cried as she passed Luke. "Tell Uncle Richard!" She rushed into the cabin. "Indians! They're hiding at the spring!"

38

The rest of the family came now and she told them about the prints. Uncle Richard said they were probably made by white men—some hunters. "Most of them wear moccasins, too."

"But I could almost see their eyes, Uncle."

"You just imagined that, Nancy. You needn't be afraid to go to the spring."

Just then a stranger ran up to the cabin, a frontiersman. "Indians!" he called softly. "I came to warn you. They're stealing horses and cattle. They're burning cabins and barns. Go to the fort at once! Hurry!"

In five minutes they were on the way. Mr. Berry went first with his gun. Then came Mrs. Berry with quilts, and after her Nancy with clothing. Behind Nancy was Ned with a bag of food. Next came Luke with ammunition and then his wife Rosie, who carried their four-year-old son, Sammie.

They went quietly. Not a word was spoken.

The fort was near, but would they reach it in time? They were all frightened.

WARRIORS CAME SCREAMING

They reached the clearing where the fort stood. The gate was opened for them and they ran in. It was closed at once and bolted on the inside. They were safe for a time.

The quilts were put on bunks in one of the small cabins. The clothing was hung on pegs in the log walls. The food was taken to the cook-cabin. Then Nancy and her cousins stood in the little yard of the fort and looked about.

"I remember this row of cabins and the look-out tower," said Nancy.

"I should think you would," Frank replied. "We've had to come here so often."

"But not for a long time, Frank."

"You're right, Nancy," said her uncle. "It has

been a long time since we had an Indian raid. I'm surprised they haven't kept their promise."

"You can't trust Indians," Frank declared.

"Don't say that, son. It isn't true. The white men made promises, too. We agreed to stay in our own land. We promised the Indians that we would never hunt on their land."

"Do you think some white men have hunted in the mountains, Father?"

"I'm afraid so, and they may have killed some Indian braves who tried to drive them away. There's some reason for this new raid into Kentucky. The Indians have been peaceful for a long time. We know that."

"Let us in!" called a man outside the stockade.

The gate was opened for the settler and his family. It was opened again for others several times. Some came on foot. Others rode their horses into the fort yard.

The horses were turned into a small fort of

their own. It had a high stockade around it. It joined the large fort, with a gate between.

The men were ready for the Indian attack. At every loophole stood a man or older boy, with his gun. The muzzle of the gun was in the hole. Another loaded gun leaned against the log wall at his side.

A woman, or girl, stood by each fighter. She was ready to reload his gun as soon as it was fired. Nancy was really too young for this, but she waited by Frank just the same.

"Are you sure you know how to reload?" Frank teased.

"Of course. Your father said I was smart about it."

"Then be smart enough to keep close to the stockade. Don't get excited and run out into the yard. That's where arrows fall, you know!"

Now the lookout shouted from the tower, "I see them! At the edge of the forest!"

"Don't shoot yet!" shouted Richard Berry. "Wait till they reach the clearing!"

The men had asked him to give the orders. He was the captain of the county militia company.

"Here they come!" the lookout shouted.

Painted warriors now rushed into the clearing, yelling and screaming.

"Fire!"

Guns blazed, bullets whined, and arrows flew. Shot after shot was fired. Suddenly the Indians turned and fled back to the forest. They carried their wounded warriors with them.

"They'll come back," a new settler declared.

"I don't think so," Mr. Berry replied. "They lost too many braves. But we won't leave the fort till we're sure."

Then a scout crept from the gate and ran quickly across the clearing. He disappeared into the forest. The settlers waited anxiously for him to return.

An hour later he reappeared from the forest. "They've gone!" he cried. "They took the trail to the mountains."

Soon the settlers started for their homes. The Berrys walked back silent and sad. The same thoughts were in each one's mind: Would their cabin be there? Had the barn been burned? Had the cattle and horses been driven away?

Nancy and her cousins ran ahead to see. "The cabin was there!" Nancy called as she came running back.

"The barn was there!" Ned called.

"The stock was all right!" Frank called.

"Thank goodness!" cried Mrs. Berry.

"We're lucky," said Mr. Berry.

"Maybe the Indians at the spring liked Nancy," Frank joked.

Nancy laughed and the others laughed with her. Frank's joke wasn't really funny. They were just glad to laugh again, at anything.

Nancy Sees
Strange Sights

THE FOLLOWING spring there was new trouble on the Berry farm. It wasn't Indians this time, however. It was crows.

"They are pulling up the corn sprouts all over the field," Mr. Berry complained. "They get them as soon as they show above the ground."

"That shows they're smart," Frank said. "They know the seed corn will be soft and tender. They don't want to eat the hard kernels."

"We'll have to replant the whole field, boys," Mr. Berry went on.

"That means a lot of hard work," Frank grumbled. "And all for a bunch of crows!"

"They'll pull up the other new sprouts, too," said Mrs. Berry.

"I can't have that. I'll have to get rid of them."

"They're not afraid of a scarecrow," Ned said. "They're roosting on the one we put up."

"They were afraid for two days," Nancy corrected. "After that they just laughed at it."

"Laughed!" exclaimed Frank.

"She's always saying that," Ned put in.

"Well, they make a different sound," Nancy explained. "They stretch out their caws, like this: Caw-aw-aw! Caw-aw-aw!"

The boys tried it but Nancy shook her head. "No! No! It's this way—Caw-aw-aw!"

Out in the barn Luke heard them cawing and laughing. "Miss Nancy is showing them how to caw," he told Sammie. "They're always having fun with her."

That evening, at supper, Mr. Berry complained again. "I've never seen so many crows.

The cornfield was black with them again this afternoon. I don't know what I'll do."

Nancy tried to defend the crows. "They weren't eating sprouts all the time, Uncle Richard. They were playing a game, too."

The others stopped eating and looked at her.

"A game!" exclaimed her uncle.

"It looked like a game to me. One of the crows found a bright-red flower. He took it in his bill and flew up high with it."

"Among trees?" Ned asked.

"No, above the field. Several crows followed him, but they always stayed some distance below. They flew close together, too. Then the first crow dropped the red flower and the others tried to catch it."

"Now, now, Nancy!" said her uncle with a smile. "You're joking."

"Ha, ha!" her cousins laughed.

"It's the truth. I saw one of the crows catch

the flower in his bill. Then he flew above the others and dropped it himself. Another crow seized it and flew up. They kept this going for a long time."

"I wish I had seen that," said Ned.

"We'll have to shoot a few of them," Mr. Berry said. "Then the others will leave."

"Oh, Uncle Richard, please don't kill them!" Nancy cried.

"I can't afford to lose my corn crop. We wouldn't have any bread this winter."

"That's true," his wife agreed.

"I'll shoot at them," Frank said. "But they'd be mighty hard to hit."

"I couldn't hit one," Ned added.

"I'll throw rocks and scare them away," Nancy offered.

"You'd need a dozen arms," her uncle said, "and they'd all have to be throwing at the same time in different directions. I'll hire a man to shoot them. There's always someone looking for work around here."

THE TRAVELING TEACHER

"A man came this morning," said Mrs. Berry the following noon, "but he was a teacher and he was looking for pupils. He had heard we had three children. Someone in the Beechland settlement told him."

"I suppose he was one of those traveling teachers," Mr. Berry replied. "There are many of them traveling about in Kentucky now."

"Well, there aren't any schools. I think it's fine these young men are willing to teach in people's cabins."

"It's a fine thing, Rachel, but traveling teachers won't find any pupils in this county," said Mr. Berry. "The boys and girls here have to help with the work."

"I'd have time to study, wouldn't I, Aunt Rachel?" Nancy asked.

"Of course, Nancy. So would the boys, this fall and winter."

"I don't want to sit in a room all day," Frank declared. "I'd rather be chopping down trees."

"So would I," said his brother.

"Mother wants me to go to school," Nancy said. "She told me so."

"I know she does," Mrs. Berry agreed. "She was hoping a traveling teacher would come to their neighborhood. Then she'd take you back home, Nancy."

"What about Indians?" Frank asked.

"She said several new settlers had moved there. They were planning to build a fort."

"I don't want you to leave," Ned told Nancy. "Frank and I wouldn't have any fun."

"I told her mother we couldn't give her up," Mrs. Berry said with a smile.

"There'll be no teacher traveling to that neighborhood till the fort is ready," Mr. Berry declared. "There aren't enough people there, and few of the people who do live there could afford to pay a teacher."

"This teacher said he'd charge three dollars a month with board and bed. He's coming back to see you this afternoon, Richard. His name is Patrick Murphy."

"Send him out to me. Maybe he'll agree to shoot crows for a time."

So it happened that all the next day shots were fired in the cornfield. Nancy covered her ears so that she couldn't hear. She couldn't bear to think of any of those beautiful black birds being killed. She didn't like to think of any animal being killed.

The second day there were only a few shots. The third day there weren't any. Every crow was gone and Mr. Murphy told Nancy that he hadn't killed many. He had just shot to scare them away.

Mr. Berry now changed his mind about school. So Patrick Murphy stayed on. He helped with the farm work in the morning. In the afternoon he had two pupils, Nancy and Ned. Frank was still too busy.

"Mr. Berry is pleased with the teacher," Luke told his wife one day. "The children are learning fast."

"Maybe so, but there's one thing I can't understand," Rosie replied. "That Mr. Murphy goes streaking off to the ravine the minute school is out. The children have noticed it, too."

"He said it was a mighty pretty spot," Luke reminded her.

"He couldn't have picked a worse one," Rosie said. "Did you tell him about the sinkhole in the ravine?"

"I did," Luke replied. "I told him about the

quicksand in it and how a colt was lost there last spring, too."

"Well, he keeps on going. There's something queer about that, Luke. No one else goes there, not even the children!"

"He told Mr. Berry it was a fine place to rest."

"Rest! Humph! He's all tired out when he comes back."

"I can't understand that. The ravine isn't far."

Now Nancy came. She said she couldn't find her dog Boots. Had they seen him?

"He was with the teacher after school," Rosie told her.

"Then he's gone to the ravine! We never take Boots there. I'm going after him!"

SICK 'EM, BOOTS! GET IT!

Nancy reached the thick growth of bushes around the ravine. She now went forward care-

54

fully. She'd have to watch for the edge of the bank or she'd fall into the sinkhole herself.

Suddenly she stopped. Why, there weren't any more bushes! They had been cut down. She saw the pile of dead brush on the bank.

She looked about and now she saw a sight that amazed her. A man was there—up in the air— walking on a rope!

The rope was high above the ground, stretched tight between two trees. But these trees were not close to the ravine. "He won't fall into it," Nancy thought.

She knew the man hadn't seen her, so she hid behind the bushes to watch. She could see him through the branches, but she couldn't see his face. He was walking away from her now.

She had never seen ropewalking before and she thought it was wonderful. She was so excited she forgot about Boots, but now he came out from the pile of brush.

At the same time the ropewalker turned his
face and Nancy saw him plainly. My goodness,
it was Master Murphy! Her teacher! Up there
in the air! My goodness' sakes alive! Her
teacher walking a rope!

Then all of a sudden a strange thing happened. The teacher's mustache came off! It fell to the ground and Boots sprang for it. The next minute he was shaking it.

Nancy almost laughed aloud—it was so funny. But Master Murphy didn't think it was funny. He climbed down a tree quickly and took his mustache from the dog's mouth.

"Sorry, old fellow," he said, "but I need those whiskers myself." He wiped it carefully and then stuck it on his upper lip.

Now he took the rope down and hid it under the brush. He put on his coat and patted the dog's head. "Come along, Boots. I don't want to be late for supper."

Nancy was the one who was late, but no one noticed because her uncle was telling a story. "The sheriff came this afternoon," he went on. "He was looking for a stranger—a tight rope walker. He was going to arrest him."

Nancy choked on her food. She wanted to look at Mr. Murphy, but she didn't dare. She heard her uncle say that the sheriff didn't know the man's name. He just knew the fellow was tall and thin with a smooth face.

"No whiskers, eh?" asked the teacher.

"Not even a mustache."

"Well, that lets me out."

"You weren't in, Master," said Mr. Berry. "You're no tightrope walker."

Again Nancy choked, and again she was afraid to look up from her plate.

"Why did the sheriff come here to look for him?" Frank asked.

"He had heard he was working in this neighborhood," said Mr. Berry.

"What had he done?" Mrs. Berry asked.

"It seems he had been walking the rope at some gathering and left without paying the tax, which was three dollars."

"That's too much for one day," Mr. Murphy declared. "The fellow wouldn't make that much in a week."

"Indeed he wouldn't!" Mr. Berry agreed. "People just put pennies in the hat when it is passed around."

"He could work at something else to pay the tax," the teacher suggested.

"He won't have a chance, Mr. Murphy. He'll have to go to jail."

"That's a shame," Mrs. Berry asserted. "It isn't fair to ask a man to walk the rope and then charge him for it."

"I agree with you on that," Mr. Murphy said.

Now supper was over and he went to his room. The others talked about the ropewalker. The boys wondered where he was working and if the sheriff would find him.

Nancy hadn't said anything yet. She hated to tell on the teacher. She didn't want him to go to jail. But she ought to tell her uncle—she didn't know what to do.

Before she could decide, Luke came into the cabin. He was so excited he stuttered. "T-t-teacher g-g-gone!" he cried. "R-r-run away!"

"A little slower, please," said Mr. Berry. "Now then, what's this about the teacher?"

"He pitched a bundle out the window. Then he jumped out and picked up the bundle and went running down the road."

"Did he have on his mustache?" Nancy asked.

"What's that?" asked Luke.

"Yes, what's that you said?" asked Mr. Berry.

Now Nancy told what she had seen in the wood. Her aunt and uncle were surprised. The boys were delighted and so was Luke.

"Sick 'em, Boots!" Frank cried.

"Get it, Boots!" shouted Ned.

Nancy's Coon Story

NED HOPED there wouldn't be any more traveling teachers coming along. He wanted to be in the forest along with his father and brother and Luke.

"It's fun to see the trees falling, and run," he said. "It's more fun than sitting on a bench all the afternoon."

"But we stood up to say our A B C's," said Nancy. "We didn't sit all the time."

"I don't call that standing. He made us toe the mark every minute. I don't want another teacher," Ned said.

She did, but she couldn't tell her aunt. Ned

wouldn't like it. So she talked to Rosie. "Do you think other teachers will come along?" she asked. "Do you think so?"

"They might and they might not. You never can tell," Rosie said.

"I know my A B C's. If I had a primer I could learn to read by myself. Master Murphy said I could. He said that was the way he learned."

"Maybe he studied his primer while he was walking the tightrope. Ha, ha!"

Nancy began to laugh, then stopped suddenly. She had just thought of something. "Rosie, maybe Uncle Richard would buy a primer for me. Do you think so?"

"I don't know about that. Money is mighty scarce out here."

"Maybe I could buy one myself. Mother gave me two pennies the last time she was here, and I already had five from Uncle Richard. Would that be enough?"

"Where would you buy it? I never saw a book in the settlement store."

"How can I get one, Rosie?"

"Maybe some new settler will bring a primer. Settlers always have a lot of things packed away in their big covered wagons."

"They wouldn't sell it to me. They'd want it for their children."

"They might lose it. It might fall out when they passed here."

"Ha, ha!" laughed Nancy.

"Ha, ha!" laughed Rosie.

Not long after this a wagon broke down in front of the Berry cabin. The new settler and his wife and children had to get out at once.

Mr. Berry helped Mr. Dix make the repairs. Mrs. Berry took Mrs. Dix and her sick baby to the cabin to rest. Nancy looked after the rest of the children.

There were five, and all girls. The oldest was

Nancy's age, and the others were from seven to four. They all had yellow hair, blue eyes and pink cheeks.

"You're all so pretty!" Nancy exclaimed.

"You're pretty, too," said the oldest girl. "I wish I had dark hair and dark eyes like yours. What's your name?"

"Nancy. I wish I had yellow hair and blue eyes. What's your name?"

"Annie. Let's play school. I've got a primer. I'll go get it."

While Annie went to the wagon the other girls told Nancy their names—Lizzie, Sallie, Susie, and Jennie.

Then Annie came with the primer, which she gave to Nancy. "You can be the teacher," she said. "I can't read."

"I can't either, but I like to hold the book. It feels good."

The youngest child, Jennie, began to cry for

her mother. Then Susie, Sallie and Lizzie cried, and Annie couldn't stop them.

"Listen, children," said Nancy. "Do you want to hear a story about a little coon?"

The girls stopped crying and nodded their yellow heads.

"Let's sit on this bank by the side of the road," Annie said. "It's nice under this beech tree."

Then the two older girls showed the younger girls where to sit. When they were all ready and comfortable, Nancy handed the primer to Annie and began her story.

WILLIE AND HIS CORN

"Once upon a time there was a little cabin in a dark forest, and in this cabin lived a boy named Willie."

"Willie who?" Annie asked.

"His folks called him Willie Johnnycake.

That was because he didn't want to eat anything else. But the day he was eleven he couldn't eat at all."

"Why couldn't he?"

"He didn't get the present he wanted, and he was disappointed. He felt so bad about it he wasn't even hungry."

"What did he want?" Lizzie asked.

"A coonskin cap with a striped tail fastened to the back. His older brother Joseph had one, and of course his father. Hunters always wore them. Every boy in the settlement had one.

" 'I'm sorry,' his mother said. 'I'd have made a cap for you if I'd had a coonskin.'

" 'I couldn't find a coon,' said his father. 'Coons used to be thicker than crows, but not any more. There are too many settlers here and too many dogs. So the coons lit out.'

" 'That's bad for me,' Willie said.

" 'It's bad for me, too,' said fourteen-year-old

Joseph. 'I need a new cap myself. Mine is worn out and I lost the tail.'

"The next week Willie's father found a baby coon in the forest. Its mother had been frightened away or killed. So this little coon was given to Willie.

" 'Take good care of it,' said his father. 'It will make a nice cap when it's older.'

"Willie made a pen for the coon, and he fed it food it liked, fish and frogs. He wanted it to grow fast. So pretty soon that little coon wasn't a baby. It was almost big enough, but its tail didn't suit Willie. It wasn't bushy enough. It wasn't growing fast enough, either. He watched that tail just as a hawk watches chickens.

"So he couldn't help seeing the rest of the coon, too. He began to notice the way it ate. He thought it was cute the way it held its food in its two forepaws.

"He was surprised at the way it cleaned its

food. It always dipped it in its pan of fresh water. It wouldn't eat one bite till this was done.

"Then Willie began to drive flies away from his own food. But he couldn't dip his johnny-cake in water, could he?"

The girls shook their heads, and Nancy went on. "Willie noticed what small bites the coon took. So pretty soon here was Willie taking small bites, too."

"I'm going to begin," said Annie gravely.

"So am I," said Susie.

"Then," said Nancy, "Willie began to think his coon was pretty. He liked its cute little face and bright eyes—and its little paws that looked like hands.

"One day the coon touched Willie's cheek with a soft little paw. That settled it. Willie wasn't going to kill his pet. No siree, he wasn't! He loved that coon!

"So now he didn't want its tail to grow. He

68

knew what would happen when it was bushy enough. His folks would say it was time to kill the coon—and they did say so, the next week.

"His father said the tail was large enough now. His mother said the stripes were broad enough, and Joseph wanted it for his own cap. 'I'll trade my hound-dog for your coon,' he said.

" 'No!' cried Willie. 'I don't want your hound-dog! I just want my coon!'

"Then Joseph offered to trade his pet fawn for the coon. He said she would follow Willie just like a dog.

" 'No!' cried Willie. 'I want my coon to follow me.'

" 'It won't! It can't! It won't be here much longer,' said Joseph.

"Then Willie knew he'd have to take his pet away. If he didn't, Joseph would kill it. But he didn't know where to hide it. He was afraid of the dark forest. He never went far into it alone."

"Why didn't he tell his father about Joseph?" Annie asked.

"It wouldn't have done any good," Nancy said. "His father thought coons were made for caps. So did his mother.

"He couldn't hide his coon at a neighbor's house because there weren't any neighbors. What could he do? He thought and thought. Then one night he decided——"

Suddenly the voice of Mr. Dix interrupted Nancy's story. "Come on, children!" he called. "The wagon is fixed now and ready to go. Here comes your mother with the baby. Pile in, girls, and we'll be off!"

"Oh, Father! I don't want to go now," said Annie. "I want to hear how the story ends."

"So do I!" cried Susie, Lizzie, Sallie, and Jennie together.

"Don't worry, girls," their father said. "We're going to live in this county. You girls can come

71

back to visit Nancy sometime and hear the rest of her story."

He hustled the girls into the wagon and helped his wife and baby in. Then he climbed up in his seat, cracked his whip, and the wagon began to roll. The girls leaned out.

"Good-by, Nancy!"

"Good-by, Annie! Good-by, girls!" Nancy cried, waving her hand.

Primer and Rag Dolls

As soon as the strangers left, Mrs. Berry went back to her loom. She was weaving now and had no time to spare.

"The boys need new suits for winter," she said. "It will take a good deal of cloth to make them, too. Frank is almost as tall as his father, and Ned has outgrown his clothes."

"My dreses are too short," said Nancy.

"I know, you're a good deal taller this year." said Mrs. Berry.

"If you keep on growing, we'll have to raise more sheep," said Frank.

Nancy didn't see him wink at Ned, so she

didn't know Frank was teasing her. "But Uncle doesn't want any more," she said.

"More sheep, more wool. More wool, more cloth. More cloth, longer skirts."

"That's funny, Frank! I wish I could remember it," Nancy said.

"If you can't, ask me. I'm always around at mealtime," he said.

"Well, be sure you do get here on time," said his mother. "Rosie will do all the cooking for a while. She won't like it if you're late."

"She doesn't want anyone in the kitchen," Ned said. "She put me out just now."

"She's not used to having others around. Remember, she's been doing outside work. She's been helping Luke with the lambs and calves."

"I can go in," Nancy said. "I help her. But she won't let Sammie in. She's afraid he'll fall in the fire."

A little later Sammie did rush into the kitchen,

and he did stumble over the pots and pans on the hearth.

"Get away from my skillets!" his mother ordered. "Keep away from my kettles! Get back from the fire!"

Sammie obeyed. Then he shouted, "She found it, Mammy! She found it!"

"Who found what?"

"Miss Nancy found the primer! The girl left it on the bank."

"For goodness' sake!" Rosie exclaimed. "I said some settler would lose it, but I was joking. Well, I reckon Miss Nancy is happy. She's got her primer at last."

"She didn't keep it. She took it back."

"Back where? Those people drove away."

"She ran after the wagon. She'll catch up with it. The horses were just walking."

"Did anyone tell her to do that—to take the book back?"

Sammie shook his head. "She lit out as soon as she picked it up."

"That's the honestest thing I ever heard of. That little girl is so honest she couldn't be any honester. Sammie, I want you to be like Miss Nancy. I don't want you acting as if you haven't got a peach in your pocket when I know you have one."

Sammie hung his head. His mother patted his hair. "Now I'm going in to tell Mrs. Berry about that primer. You go to the orchard and get yourself another nice ripe peach."

THE END OF THE STORY

Almost an hour had passed and Nancy hadn't returned. Her aunt was worried. "It wouldn't take her long to catch up with the wagon," she said. "I'm sure Mr. Dix would stop when he saw her coming."

"The children would be sure to see her, too," said Mr. Berry.

"She's been gone too long. I don't like her to be out on the road alone, even in broad daylight," Mrs. Berry added.

"I'll go to meet her, Mother," Frank offered.

"Take your gun," said his father.

"Why? Are you worried about Indians?"

"I am now, Frank, and I will be until we have real peace with them."

Just then Nancy came in. She had been running and was out of breath.

"Were you frightened?" asked her aunt. "We knew you took the primer back."

"No, I hurried home because I knew you'd be worried about me," Nancy said. "The girls made me stay awhile. They wanted to know how my story ended. That was the story I told them out on the bank."

"I heard the first part of it," said Ned. "I was

behind the bushes. I told the others. You made it up, didn't you?"

"Of course," Nancy replied. "I made up the ending for the girls."

"How did it end?"

"Guess."

"We've been guessing," said her aunt. "But we couldn't decide what Willie finally did with his coon."

"Go on and tell us," said Ned.

"Do you all want to hear?"

"Yes! Yes!"

Nancy was pleased. She sat on a stool facing them and began:

"Well, Willie decided to run away. So the next morning he left at sunrise. The coon sat on his shoulder. Its beautiful striped tail hung down his back.

"He wished the settlement boys could see it, but he didn't dare go that way. His brother

78

would find out and follow him, so he took the trail through the forest."

"Wait a minute!" cried Ned. "You said he was afraid of the forest."

"He was, but he loved his pet so much he went into the forest anyhow. It was dark there, but he went on and on and on.

"At last he came to a creek and stopped. He found a small cave in the bank and moved in quick. He didn't want any hunter to see him and tell his folks.

"It was a fine place for the coon. It could get its own fish and frogs. It got enough for Willie, too. All he had to do was to cook his share."

The others laughed. Then Nancy went on:

"Willie had a hard time at first, though. The coon wouldn't let him track one thing into the cave—no dirt, no grass, no leaves, no fish scales, nothing. If he did, the coon would sweep it out with its tail."

The others laughed again, and Aunt Rachel said the coon was a good housekeeper.

"It was better than Willie's mother," Nancy said. "She didn't worry when Willie tracked dirt into their cabin, but the coon just wouldn't have it."

"Did it speak to Willie about this?" Frank asked, teasing her.

"It didn't need to," Nancy replied. "Willie didn't want it to wear its tail off sweeping. So he was mighty careful."

"Ha, ha!" laughed the Berrys.

"That cute little fellow was busy all day. He fished and washed his food. He cleaned the cave and he cleaned himself. After a while Willie wanted to be clean, too. He began to wash behind his ears."

"Did he ever take a bath?" Frank asked with a wink at Ned.

"Well, he was going to," Nancy said. " 'Come

Sunday,' he said to himself, 'I'll take a bath in the creek.'

"But on Saturday something happened. His father found the cave and Willie and the coon. A hunter had told him.

"'Come home, son,' he said. 'Your brother doesn't want your pet now. He found another coon and he's satisfied. Also, your ma's going to make you a cap from a sheep's skin.'

"So Willie and his pretty coon went back home. And that's all."

The others laughed and said it was a good story. They said Nancy was smart to think it up all by herself.

Nancy didn't pay much attention to this. There was something else on her mind. Now she took a little book from her big pocket and held it up.

"Look!" she exclaimed. "It's the primer! The Dixes gave it to me. Mrs. Dix said their kin

back home would send them another. I just had
to take it, Aunt Rachel."

"Of course you did. It wouldn't have been
polite to refuse."

"Now I can learn to read, and then I won't
have to make up stories. I can read them."

"I hope a teacher will come," her aunt said.
"You'll learn faster with help, Nancy."

MELISSA AND LILYBELL

The following week some friends came from
the Beechland settlement to spend the day. They
were Mr. and Mrs. Paddock and their nine-year-
old daughter Ella. They had been invited, but
even so the work couldn't stop.

The visitors knew this, so they just pitched in
and helped. Company was supposed to do that
in Kentucky in 1792.

Mr. Paddock helped Mr. Berry repair a

82

wagon wheel. Mrs. Paddock helped Mrs. Berry with her weaving. The two girls worked together until Nancy's chores were finished. Then they took their rag dolls to the yard and sat under a great beech tree.

Nancy called her doll Melissa. Ella called hers Lilybell. The girls pretended they were bringing them from Virginia in baskets.

"Melissa says her legs hurt. I guess I'll have to walk her about," said Nancy.

"I'll lift Lilybell out so she can walk with her. Her legs hurt bad."

Just then they saw Ned coming and they knew what would happen. He always teased them about their dolls.

"He tried to grab them the last time I came," Ella said.

"Let's give them to Rosie. She'll hide them," Nancy said.

They started toward the kitchen, but they

were too slow. Ned caught up with them and grabbed both dolls and ran.

The girls ran after him, but they couldn't run as fast. All of a sudden Ned disappeared. They didn't know where he had gone. So they sat on a log and waited.

"He'll lose Melissa's shoes," Nancy said. "They're pretty too. Aunt Rachel made them from cornhusks."

"I'm afraid Lilybell's eyes will fall out," Ella said. "They're just black watermelon seeds pasted on."

The girls had a right to be worried. Most frontier women didn't have any time to make dolls. A frontier girl who had one was lucky, and she couldn't expect to get another.

Help was near, however. Luke had seen Ned grab the dolls, and he knew where the girls were waiting. So now he stopped Ned when he ran into the barn to hide them.

"Where are you taking the dolls, Ned?" he asked. "What are you going to do?"

"I'm taking them up to the loft to hide them under the hay," Ned said. "The girls will never find them there. Ha, ha, ha!"

"You oughtn't to do that. The hay will pull their hair off."

"It's nothing but shaving curls."

"The girls think it's pretty."

"Pretty! Humph! I suppose they think this bunch of rags is pretty, too."

"They sure do. They love their dolls. You'd better give them back, Ned. The girls are sitting out there on a log."

Ned had always obeyed Luke. His father had told him to. "Maybe I won't now," he thought. "I'm older now." So he said he didn't have to give the dolls back and wasn't going to, not until he got ready, anyway.

Luke looked at the boy with his kind dark

86

eyes. Then he spoke firmly. "March yourself out there and hand over the dolls."

Ned marched, and he handed over the dolls. "Here they are," he said. "I didn't hurt them. They're just as ugly as ever. Ha, ha!"

Then he ran away fast so that he wouldn't hear what the girls said.

Indian Raids
and Militia Drill

NANCY STUDIED her primer all summer. By fall
of 1792 when she was almost nine she could
make out words. But she couldn't read lines
and she was discouraged.

"I wish you had a teacher to help you," her
Aunt Rachel said one evening. "I've been hoping one of those traveling teachers would stop
here, but none has come by."

"I was told they weren't traveling through
Kentucky now," Mr. Berry said.

"Are they afraid to come here?" his wife
asked. "On account of the Indians?"

"I suppose so and I don't blame them. There's

no real peace between us and the Cumberland Mountain Indians."

"They haven't bothered us for a long time."

"I guess they've heard that you're the captain of the militia company," Nancy said gravely.

Her uncle smiled. "The warriors wouldn't be afraid of me, but they might fear a fight with our militia."

"I believe they do," Mrs. Berry said. "Look how they are attacking the settlers near the Cumberland Mountains. There is no militia to protect the people there."

"There aren't enough settlers out there in southeastern Kentucky to form a company," Frank declared.

"You're right, son," his father agreed. "Those people shouldn't have gone so far away from settlements. Now they are coming back, and a good many have decided to stay in this county."

"I'm glad of that!" Mrs. Berry exclaimed. "I

hope the men will join your militia company, Richard. The more men you have in your company, the safer we should be from Indians."

"I'm going to ask them. I have arranged to meet them at the mill in the morning."

The next morning all the newcomers promised to join the militia. They said their sons would join also, every one over fifteen.

"We'd better get ready to fight," one man declared. "Those Indians will be coming here before long."

"I can't believe that!" the miller exclaimed. "We are too far from the Cumberland Mountains, where they live."

"That won't keep them away now, sir. They'll raid every part of Kentucky. They are bitter against all whites."

"I know the reason," said another newcomer. "An Indian told me while we were hunting together. He was my friend and I know he spoke

90

the truth. He said some white men had come up into the mountains and had killed many braves."

"They had no right to go there," Mr. Berry said. "That land belongs to the Indians. Why did the white men go?"

"They tried to take silver from an old mine up there," said the first new settler. "They knew the Indians had used the silver from that mine for their chains and bracelets for years."

"What happened?" asked the miller.

"There was a fight. Some white men were killed and many braves."

"No wonder these Indians hate white men!" Mr. Berry exclaimed.

"Well, that trouble is over," the miller said.

"No, it isn't over," the newcomer asserted. "I have been asked to guide a party of miners to that mine, but I refused."

"They must not go!" Mr. Berry said. "Do you know who they are?"

"I don't know their names, but they are all in this county now. They are getting ready to go."

"They must be stopped. Our lives depend on it. I'll tell the sheriff at once!"

Mr. Berry jumped on his horse and galloped away. The newcomers were surprised.

"He went in a hurry," one said.

"He acts in a hurry if it's necessary," the miller explained. "And don't think he was scared about his own safety. He was thinking about his wife and three children."

"Two children and a niece," the cooper corrected. "But she's the same as his own child. He thinks the world of her."

BIG BEETS AND BIG TALK

It was the day of the militia drill. It was to be held in the meadow by the gristmill. Everyone in the county was expected, and almost everyone in the county was there when the Berrys finally arrived in their wagon.

"I'm glad they came," Mr. Berry said. "It will give them courage to know we are ready to defend them from Indians."

"They'll have fun, too," said Frank. "They'll see wrestlers, a tightrope walker, and a bear that really dances."

"I want to see the bear dance," Nancy said.

"Don't go too close. He might try to hug you."

Nancy and Ned thought this was very funny. But they stopped laughing quickly when they heard the drums and fifes on the clearing they called the drill grounds.

They were proud of Captain Berry marching at the head of his company. They were proud of Frank when he came marching along.

"I'll be with them as soon as I'm fifteen," Ned said proudly.

At noon the Berrys and their kin ate together. Then Nancy went with her girl cousins to see the sights.

They went to see the dancing bears first, but they were all disappointed. "It didn't really dance," one girl complained. "It just stood on its hind legs and turned around."

"It didn't want to do that," said Nancy. "I could tell by the way it grunted."

The girls watched tumblers, wrestlers, and a tightrope walker. This last man scared Nancy.

She was afraid his mustache would fall off, but it didn't.

After this the girls joined a crowd of people. A man was telling about Daniel Boone, so the girls stayed to listen.

"Well," the speaker said, "I reckon you all know that Daniel Boone was one of the first men to come to Kentucky, and you know what he thought of it, too. 'Why, Bill,' he said to me, 'there's nothing like that country in the whole round world.'

"He said it had the tallest trees, and the largest caves and the bluest grass he ever saw. He said it had the biggest birds and the biggest fish and the biggest beets."

The crowd laughed. Then the speaker continued: "Daniel told me that it took three yokes of oxen to pull one beet out of the ground."

"Ha, ha, ha, ha!" laughed the crowd, and Nancy and her cousins laughed with them.

"That's not the end of the story, folks. I suppose you'd like to know about the hole that was left, wouldn't you?"

"Yes! Yes!"

"Well, sir," the man went on, "Daniel said the hole was so big a buffalo could wallow in it. And he said he saw six boys swimming in it after a rain one day."

While the crowd laughed and clapped, Nancy heard her uncle ask one settler what the man's name was.

"I don't know, Captain. He's a stranger here. No one knows him."

Just then a man called out, "Tell another Boone story, mister!"

"I'll be glad to, but this one won't be funny," the man went on. "Daniel was serious when he told me this. 'Bill,' he said to me one day, 'every man in Kentucky can get rich quick. He won't have to break his back clearing land for crops.

96

He won't have to plow the land when he's shaking with ague.'"

The people nodded. They knew all about hard work and ague.

Then the speaker went on: "'There's riches in these mountains,' Daniel said. 'There's enough silver to fill every man's pocket.'"

"How did he know that?" a man asked.

"He saw a silver mine. The Indians were using the silver to make chains and bracelets."

"Do you know where it is?"

"I do. Daniel told me."

"Where? Where?" cried excited voices.

"Wait a minute, mister!" Mr. Berry cried. "I want to ask you a question."

"Go ahead!"

"Why didn't Daniel Boone get rich on that silver mine himself? He's still a poor man."

"He's still breaking his back to clear land, too," added a farmer.

"I'll tell you the reason!" the speaker shouted. "Several white men did try to dig that silver, but the Indians killed or wounded most of them."

"Then how do you expect these settlers to dig it?" Mr. Berry asked.

"They could be guarded by the militia. Every county could send its militia company. Isn't it the duty of the militia to protect citizens of this state from danger?"

"Yes, it is to protect them from savages. We are willing to die for that. But we are not willing to die so that a few men can steal silver from the Indians."

"Hooray!" shouted the militiamen.

"It isn't stealing," shouted the speaker.

"It is! It is!" cried voices.

"It isn't! It isn't!" cried other voices.

Men began to argue and quarrel. The crowd took sides. There were loud voices, shouts and angry yells. There was so much confusion no one saw the speaker slip away from the gathering and go into the forest.

Mr. Berry hurried to Nancy and her cousins. "I'm afraid there'll be fighting and men will be hurt. Go to the other side of the grounds, over by the forest."

THE TUNE HE PLAYED TOO OFTEN

"There's nothing over here but a fiddler," a girl said, "and there's no one listening to him."

"I want to listen," said Nancy.

"But we can't have any fun here," another cousin said.

So after a while they wandered away—all but Nancy. She loved music so much she couldn't go. She found a shady spot near the fiddler and sat on the grass to listen.

She was surrounded by bushes, but she could hear the music. When she parted the bushes, she

99

could see the fiddler, too, sitting in the shade
of a near-by tree.

After a time she began to wonder about two
things. Why was he away over here on the edge
of the woods? And why did he play the same tune
every other time?

The song that he played over and over was a
song she knew, called "The Horse Cave Gallop."
Frank liked to sing it. Nancy sang it now to
herself while the fiddler played.

"Now, gallop and run to the cave in the hill!
  You'll be safe enough there, my Dolly and Bill,
  My Stepper and Queenie, my Star and my
    Pride,
  No brave will find you so deep inside.

"Faster! Yet faster, my galloping steeds!
  Braves may be hiding among those reeds.
  They'll rope you and tie you and lead you away
  From me who have loved you for many a day.
  So faster and faster and faster, until
  You're safe, my pets, in the cave in the hill."

100

Now Nancy began to notice another strange thing. When the fiddler played other tunes, no one came. But when he played "The Horse Cave Gallop," one or two men always hurried up.

They didn't listen to the music. In fact, the fiddler would stop playing and talk to them for a moment or two. Then the men would nod and hurry away.

Nancy couldn't understand this. She went closer and stood behind a tree.

Now the fiddler was playing that "Gallop" again, but no one was coming. Yes, here was a man! He was coming from the woods. Nancy was surprised to see that it was the speaker!

"He's acting queer, too," she thought. "He's darting from tree to tree as if he didn't want to be seen. But he's waving to the fiddler."

"For goodness' sakes!" she exclaimed. "The fiddler has joined him. They've gone into the forest together."

She meant to tell her uncle about this, but the family was ready to leave when she went back to the meadow. As soon as they were on their way, Uncle Richard began to talk about the fight.

"It was pretty bad for a time, but the sheriff stopped it," he said. "It was the speaker's fault. He tried to get the crowd excited about that silver mine."

"I guess he thought the people would force the militia to go to the mine," Frank said.

"Of course," said his father. "That was his game. He was one of the silver gang, I'm sure."

"Why didn't the sheriff arrest him for causing trouble?" asked Mrs. Berry.

"He wanted to, but the man had disappeared," Mr. Berry replied. "The sheriff and his men searched the grounds for him, too, but they couldn't find him."

"I know where he is," said Nancy. Then she told her uncle what she had seen and heard.

102

"So, this fiddler played 'The Horse Cave Gallop' over and over, did he?"

"Yes, Uncle Richard."

"I think you may have discovered a secret, Nancy. Maybe the gang has been meeting in Horse Cave. Probably that tune brought them to the fiddler and he told them when the next meeting would be held."

"Are you going to tell the sheriff about him?" asked Frank.

"As soon as I can find him," said his father. "Nancy, we can all be thankful to you, and to your ear for music."

"She figured things out, too," Frank declared.

"She's good at that," Ned said.

Plans to Seize Nancy

FLAMING TORCHES lighted the inky blackness of Horse Cave. They shone on the ten men sitting on the ground around their leader, Ed Peters. William Horn had just told them about escaping from the sheriff yesterday at the drill.

"Are you sure no one saw you enter the wood?" asked the leader.

"No one. I'm sure of that."

"That's right," said the fiddler, Amos Fry. "There wasn't anyone about when he came back for me, either."

"A guard is watching at the river ford. He'll warn us if anyone comes this way. Now what about this militia captain, Richard Berry? You said he didn't like your speech yesterday, Horn."

"He certainly didn't. He said that we had no right to the silver and that the militia would not fight Indians to protect our miners."

"The men in his company agreed with him, too," added Fry.

"That's bad!" exclaimed Peters. "We need him and his men. We can't work the mines without them. He must be forced to change his mind somehow."

"Yes! Yes! Force him!" cried voices.

"It might be done through his family," Peters went on. "I was told he had two sons and a young niece. One of them could disappear, with our help. What do you think?"

The members nodded and showed they agreed. Peters went on: "We could make it look as if Indians were to blame. We'd leave Indian signs on trails."

"What kind of signs?" a member asked.

"Old moccasins and torn hunting shirts. Indians always throw things away when they travel. Every frontiersman knows that."

"Everyone knows what Mr. Berry would do, too," said Horn. "He'd follow those signs clear to the mountains. And certainly his militia company would go with him."

Again members nodded in agreement.

"Then we'd follow with our men and open the mine," said Peters. "The militia would have to protect us then. They wouldn't dare to let Indians kill us. Every white man in Kentucky would be angry if they did."

"I'm in favor of taking Mr. Berry's niece, Nancy Hanks," said the fiddler. "I live near some of her kinfolk in Nelson County. I know all about her."

"No!" exclaimed Matt Wilson. "I'm in favor of taking one of his sons. They are older."

"Wait a minute, Matt! I haven't finished about the girl. She isn't too young—she's almost nine. Besides, she's got a lot of men kin in Nelson County, in the Hanks families, and they all belong to a militia company over there. They'd get it out quick if the girl was captured."

"Then we'd have two companies to protect our miners," said Peters. "The Indians couldn't fight that many men with guns."

"I say we get the girl," said a member.

"Yes! Yes!" voices cried.

"No!" Matt shouted again. "I've got a daughter her age. I won't consent till I know what you're planning to do when you get her."

"We could hide her for a time," Horn suggested. "Then we could take her to the mountains and turn her loose near her uncle's camp. She'd think she escaped from Indians. We'd be dressed like them."

"Where will you hide her?"

"In some cave."

"That could be mighty dangerous, mister. There's an underground river in nearly every one of these caves. Just one misstep and she'd fall into icy cold water. She'd never get out."

"We won't hide her in that kind. I'll find one that's dry, if it's my job."

"It is your job," said the leader. "You and Fry can manage the thing. Get this girl as soon as you can."

Matt Wilson stood. "I'm against it," he declared sharply. "That is, I am if there's to be any rough business."

"There won't be," Horn replied. "We'll get her when she's alone—maybe in the orchard, or when she goes to the spring."

"We'll paint our faces like Indian warriors," Fry told them.

"You'll scare her to death," Matt grumbled.

"That can't be helped, sir," said the leader.

109

Now the guard entered quickly. "The sheriff is coming with a posse!" he cried. "They've reached the river!"

"Go! Go!" ordered the leader. "Jump on your horses and ride fast!"

So Horse Cave was empty when the sheriff arrived with his men and Mr. Berry.

INDIAN SIGNS FOUND

Soon after this the Berrys had visitors. Three of the Hanks boys stopped at the farm. They said they had been hunting in Washington County. Now they were on their way back to Nelson County.

Couldn't Nancy go back with them? Her mother wanted her to come for a long visit. She could stay all winter if she wanted to.

"She isn't here just now," said Mrs. Berry. "She went after walnuts with Frank and Ned.

They took their lunch. So they won't come back till afternoon."

"We could go after her," offered Joseph, age seventeen. "Where are the walnut trees?"

"They're on our farm," Mr. Berry replied, "but I'm afraid we can't allow Nancy to travel now. It wouldn't be safe."

The three young men were puzzled. They said there was no danger from Indians. It was almost winter and Indians didn't leave their villages then. Everyone knew this.

"I thought that myself until this afternoon. A hunter brought a moccasin here. He had found it on the trail near by."

"Couldn't it belong to a white man?" asked William, aged sixteen.

"This one couldn't. It was the kind the Cumberland Mountain Indians wear—the tribe that lives near the silver mine."

"We women can't make such moccasins,"

Mrs. Berry explained. "The bead pattern is too difficult to copy."

"I sent a man to guard Nancy and the boys," Mr. Berry said, "and I gave him my gun!"

Joseph turned to his brothers. "We'd better leave Nancy here, boys."

Charles, aged fifteen, forgot to be polite. "We can't be bothered with a girl. These Indians may attack us."

"You can fight them off," Mr. Berry said. "I've heard you were quick with your guns."

Well, yes, they were, but they'd come for Nancy again sometime, they said. They rode away in a hurry.

It was suppertime when the nut pickers returned. Nancy was sorry she had missed her cousins. "I wanted to tell them about my primer," she said. "I wanted them to know I could read it—a little."

"I'll take you to Nelson County, Nancy," said

Frank. "How would you like to go tomorrow if it's a good day?"

"Nancy isn't going any place just now," said his father. "Neither are you and Ned." Then he told them about the Indian sign.

"I suppose we'll have to carry our guns to the fields," Frank said.

"Yes, everywhere. One of us will stand guard while the others work."

"Will there ever come a time when we won't be afraid?" Mrs. Berry asked.

"It may take war, Rachel. Men are saying that everywhere, but I am hoping for peace as soon as these silver men are in jail."

"They haven't been found yet."

"They'll make some kind of a move soon. They'll have to, to carry out their plans."

"Have you any idea what their plans are?" asked Mrs. Berry.

"Some scheme to get that silver. Just now I'm

113

more worried about Indians. You and Nancy must not go far away from the cabin. Don't ever go to the orchard alone. It's too close to the forest."

"I'll warn Rosie and Sammie."

"By all means! We wouldn't want them captured, Rachel."

"I'd rather they captured me," Nancy said.

"Shall I tell the braves that?" Frank asked with a smile.

"Ha! Ha!" Ned laughed. "Answer that one if you can, Nancy."

"I meant it," Nancy said gravely.

HE CREPT TOWARD HER

No one remembered Nancy's new pet out in the orchard. Nancy had found it only a few days ago. It was out in the orchard because Aunt Rachel had said she must keep it there.

114

"But it's so pretty," Nancy had said. "It has lovely soft black fur, and there's a white stripe all the way down its back."

"No matter," Aunt Rachel had said firmly.

"She has a pretty face and her eyes are blue, too," Nancy had said.

"She's still a skunk," Aunt Rachel had said. "You can't bring it any closer to the cabin."

Nancy fed and watered her skunk just before her own supper. Now she remembered it. She could not ask one of the boys to go with her because they were milking, and Rosie was busy.

"I can't let Blueyes go hungry," she thought. "It won't take five minutes." Nothing could happen in that time. Her uncle was just scared on account of that moccasin.

Then she had an idea. If Indians left it, they had gone on. Of course! They'd be miles away by now. Her uncle hadn't thought of that.

Nancy filled a pan with water and then hurried

115

to the orchard. While she was giving Blueyes its water she saw a green plant growing on the forest side. "Blueyes would like some of those leaves," she thought.

She waded through tall dead grass toward the plant. At the same time two men were hiding at the edge of the forest. They looked like Indian warriors, but Nancy did not see them.

They had been waiting since noon to find Nancy alone. Now she was walking straight toward them. A moment later one crept from behind a tree. The other stayed there on guard.

Nancy reached the plants. As she stooped to pull off leaves, an Indian seized her. He put his hand over her mouth so she couldn't scream. Then he pulled her toward the forest.

Nancy struggled, but he held her tight. As soon as they reached the wood, he stopped and took his hand from her mouth.

"No scream—no harm," he said. "You scream

—tie up." He showed her the rope he carried. She looked at it and at that hideous face and she was terrified.

The man pointed to a path. "That way—go!"

Nancy started, but she was so frightened she couldn't walk. She sank down to the ground. The man bent over to lift her. Then two white hunters sprang out from behind trees and seized him by the arms.

"Run, Nancy, run!" one cried. "Call your uncle! We'll hold this fellow!"

The man struggled fiercely. Nancy could hear the noise as she ran. Her family heard her screams and ran from cabin, stable, and barn. She had reached the clearing now, and behind her came the hunters with the man. They were holding his arms firmly.

"That Indian tried to get me!" Nancy cried. "He dragged me into the forest!"

"This man is no Indian," said one of the

hunters. "He's one of the silver gang. He's the fiddler who was playing at the mill."

Nancy was astonished. She looked at the man closely. She hardly heard what the hunters were telling the others. "He is the fiddler!" she cried. "He played 'The Horse Cave Gallop' at the drill the other day!"

"That's right," a hunter agreed. "A member of the gang told the sheriff about him and his partner. It was Matt Wilson. So the sheriff sent us to watch them."

"He'll do his fiddling in jail for a good long time," said Mr. Berry.

"Indeed he will!" said a hunter. "That partner of his will be with him, too. We've got him tied to a tree back there."

"The sheriff will be pleased to see both of them," said Mr. Berry.

"Maybe the rest of the gang will leave when they learn these men are in jail," said Mrs. Berry.

"I hope so. This county would be better off without such men."

"It's a pity the sheriff can't put them all in jail," said her husband. "They'll be sure to make the Indians angry if they try to mine that silver."

"Do you suppose they left that moccasin on the trail the other day?" asked Frank.

"Probably," said one of the hunters. "That would make us think the Indians were going to attack us. Then we'd go to war against the Indians, and the silver gang could work their mine in safety."

War!

In the spring and summer of 1793, canoes filled with warriors were seen on Kentucky streams. They were on their way to join the Ohio River tribes in a war against the white settlers. The leader of all these Indians was the great Chief Little Turtle.

There were hundreds of warriors, and not enough settlers to fight them. So the President of the United States sent an army into the Ohio country. This army was commanded by the famous officer General Anthony Wayne.

General Wayne's camp was near Cincinnati on the Ohio River. He didn't have enough soldiers to fight warriors from so many tribes, so he called for volunteers.

At once Kentucky men started for Wayne's camp. Even youths under sixteen volunteered. Frank Berry was among these.

There were some things about this war that puzzled Nancy. She was asking Ned questions now. "Why did the Cumberland Mountains Indians go into the war? Those silver men were put in jail. Didn't the Indians know that?"

"Their chief was told, but they joined the other tribes anyway. All of them hate white people. They are determined to drive every settler out of Kentucky and Ohio."

"What would we do if they won, Ned? Where would we go?"

"They won't win, Nancy. They can't beat Anthony Wayne. He was one of George Washington's best officers during the War of the Revolution. He'll outsmart the Indians."

Now young volunteers were passing almost every day. Each one carried a long Kentucky rifle and wore a coonskin cap. Some rode horses, but most walked.

Most stopped to rest under the beech trees in front of the Berry cabin, too. Then Nancy would come with a bucket of cold spring water. The young men were grateful for the water and always thanked her.

Today, while a group was drinking and passing the gourd dipper, they talked about the war. Nancy heard them as she waited near by.

"I met a teamster who had just come back from General Wayne's camp," a youth began. "He had been hauling corn up there and he found out a lot of things."

"Go on and tell!"

"He said Little Turtle's warriors had been trying to surprise Wayne's troops. They had been seen slipping around Wayne's camp at night."

"They thought they could creep in and take our soldiers by surprise," another youth said.

"And kill every one of them," added still another youth.

"But it didn't turn out that way," the first went on. "The Indian spies always found our camp-fires burning and guards marching about."

"Hurrah!"

"So Little Turtle and his men found they couldn't surprise Anthony Wayne, and they gave him a new name. They called him 'the man-who-never-sleeps.' "

"The General should be proud of that name," a volunteer declared. "I know I would be."

Presently the volunteers were gone, but Nancy remembered their words.

"I'm proud of General Wayne," she said at dinner. "The Indians won't take Frank by surprise."

Then she told what the volunteer had said,

and Frank's parents were happier than they had been since their son left home.

"You've made me feel better, Nancy," her aunt said. "I'm thankful that you remembered. Now I know Frank will be taken care of."

"I'm thankful, too," her uncle said. Then he patted his niece's hand fondly.

GOOD SHOOTERS AND WAR WORKERS

The next day Nancy saw the Hanks boys coming. They were riding horses and they wore coonskin caps and carried long rifles. She ran to the gate and waited until they had drawn rein.

"Light and tie!" she cried as they approached. "Light and tie!"

They smiled at her. Then they "lighted" and tied their horses to beech-tree branches. After this they followed Nancy into the cabin.

"Well, we're bound for the war," Joseph told

the Berrys. "I'm thinking General Wayne will be mighty pleased to see us coming. We're the best shots in Nelson County."

"We're the best in the State of Kentucky," William declared.

"We're the best in the United States," Charles bragged. "Grandma always said that, and I believed her."

The family laughed. Then Joseph went on bragging. "I'm aiming to shoot the earring off Little Turtle's ear."

"I'll shoot off the ring in his other ear," William bragged.

"I'll aim at his feathers," Charles said.

The family laughed again. Then dinner was ready and there was no more joking. The boys talked gravely about the war.

When the Hanks boys finally left, Joseph was carrying on his horse a large bag of walnuts which Ned was sending to Frank. In his saddle-

bag William had wool stockings for Frank from
his mother.

In Charlie's pocket was Nancy's gift, her seven
cents. "Tell Frank they're all I had," she had
whispered to Charlie.

"He'll be glad to get them, Nancy," Charlie
had whispered back.

Then the three brothers rode away smiling and turning to wave. The family waved until they disappeared in the forest.

"They'll make fine soldiers," said Mr. Berry. "You can be proud of them, Nancy."

"I am. I'm proud to be kin to them."

Before long winter came, the winter of 1793-1794. There were light snows and cold winds out of the north. Now no more volunteers passed by on their way to the war.

Sammie was worried about this. He was always asking why no more soldiers came by. One day his father tried to explain.

"All's gone that's going," Luke said. "Now General Wayne is busy showing them how to fight Indians. He doesn't want them to get scared and run away when the fighting starts."

"What's going to scare them?"

"The warriors, son. They paint their faces so they'll look mean, and some wear horns."

128

"Like the devil?"

"Like a thousand devils!"

"I'd be scared," said Rosie.

"I wouldn't," Sammie bragged.

Luke smiled. "You're scared of a woodpile after dark."

"He's scared of a woodpile anytime," said his mother.

"You must do your share of the work, Sammie," Luke said gravely. "You must help keep the wood box in the kitchen filled."

"We're all working extra hard now," he added. "Look how Miss Nancy is doing outside work. She goes to the pasture when it's pouring down rain, or maybe snowing and sleeting hard."

"Look how she rides that balky old mule to the mill," Rosie told the boy. "Mr. Berry gave his horses to the army, and they're doing war work now, pulling heavy cannon."

"That's a fact, Sammy," Luke said. "Are you

going to let those horses think they're better Kentuckians than you?"

"No, sir!" said Sammie. "From now on I'm going to keep that wood box filled. I don't care if I am scared."

Then his mother kissed him on the cheek, and his father patted him on the head. "Good for you, Sammie," they said.

WAITING FOR NEWS

There was no visiting now between relatives. Warriors might be on the forest trails. Nancy hadn't seen her mother since the war began and she was worried.

"We'll take you to see her as soon as it's safe," Mr. Berry told Nancy. "There's sure to be a battle this spring. General Wayne has said he would attack the Indian force then."

"Will that end the war, Father?"

"I believe it will, Ned."

The spring of 1794 came and passed, but there was no news of a battle. Summer came and there was still no news. Everyone was worried now. What did the silence mean? Had the Indians won the war?

Nancy heard men asking these questions at the mill. This was when she was waiting for her corn to be ground. She heard the same kind of talk at the store in the Beechland settlement. She was ten and one half now, so she understood the danger. She knew what would happen if Chief Little Turtle was victorious.

One night Nancy dreamed about him. She told the family at breakfast. "I saw him plainly," she said. "His face wasn't painted and he didn't look a bit mean. He had large hoop earrings in his ears and a feather in his hair."

"Then the Hanks boys didn't aim right," Mr. Berry said.

Nancy laughed and then went on: "Anyway he smiled at me and then he gave me a present. What do you think it was?"

The others said they couldn't guess.

"It was a First Reader! He said he'd teach me to read it. Then I woke up."

"Ha, ha!" Ned laughed. "Did he say he'd scalp you if you missed words?"

Everyone laughed but Mrs. Berry. "Your dream frightens me Nancy," she said gravely. "It could mean that Little Turtle had won the war—and that he was ready to teach all white people a lesson."

Nancy was puzzled. "Do you mean a lesson in a book, Aunt Rachel?" she asked.

"No, it wouldn't be that nice," Aunt Rachel replied. "It would be stories of cabins burned and white people fleeing for their lives everywhere on the frontier."

"I don't believe in dreams," Mr. Berry de-

132

clared firmly. "They don't mean anything at all. They're just jumbled-up nonsense, and there's no sense worrying about them."

"I hope you're right, Richard, but I'm not sure," Mrs. Berry said. "I'll never be sure until news come and we know the truth."

It was late summer before the Berrys had any news about the fighting. Then a soldier came riding up to the cabin one day.

"Good news!" he shouted. "General Anthony Wayne has won a big battle! Little Turtle and his warriors fled!"

Mr. Berry sighed with relief. "Now we can live in peace," he said. "There will be no more trouble with Indians now."

"Oh, I'm so thankful!" Rachel Berry exclaimed. "Now Frank will come home again and everything will be as it used to be."

"I'm thankful, too," Nancy said. Then she cried because she was so happy.

Frank Comes and Nancy Goes

Nancy was past eleven when the volunteers began to pass by the farm again. Now they were going the other way. They stopped for a drink of water, but they didn't rest long. They were in a hurry to get home.

Then one day Frank Berry came. His family was delighted to see him so well and strong. No one worked that day. They listened to the young soldier talk. He told a story that surprised them.

"The Indians almost won the war," he stated.

"What!" exclaimed his father.

"It's a fact. The day of the battle some warriors had captured one of our supply wagons.

134

It was partly filled with clothing for the soldiers
—uniforms and hats.

"The warriors were delighted with their loot.
They forgot they were fighting a war. They ac-
tually stopped to try on the coats and hats."

"While the battle was going on?" asked his
mother in surprise.

"Right in the midst of it. Chief Little Turtle
had to send for them. He said he and his force
were being surrounded by soldiers.

"The warriors started back, but they were
stopped in their tracks. And who do you think
stopped them? The Kentucky Volunteers!"

"Hooray!" cried the others.

"I was with them. So were Joseph, William
and Charles. No one could reload as fast as
those boys."

"Hooray!" Nancy cried.

"Well, we chased those braves so far they
couldn't get back. And before long General

Wayne had the other warriors running, and their chief was fleeing with them."

Nancy and Ned laughed and clapped their hands. Mr. Berry put his hand on Frank's shoulder. "I'm proud you had a part in it, Frank."

"I, too, am proud of you, son," said his mother. "You helped to make this country safe. Or will we be safe? The tribes might start another war."

"They can't, Mother. General Wayne said they couldn't. They lost too many braves, and we captured nearly all their guns. You needn't be afraid to ride on the trails any more. There'll be no arrows flying."

"Now we can build roads," Mr. Berry declared. "We've already made plans for a church and school in the settlement."

"School!" Nancy exclaimed. "A real schoolhouse, Uncle Richard?"

"Yes, indeed. We'll begin cutting trees this week for the logs."

136

"Am I going?"

"You are and so is Ned."

"I might go myself," Frank said. "Have you found a teacher?"

"A young man has promised to teach here."

"Then I can't go to visit Mother now, and my stepfather is coming for me Sunday."

"The tree haven't been chopped down yet, Nancy," said Mrs. Berry. "You'll have plenty of time for a visit."

"No, not plenty, Rachel. There will be several men working. It won't take long to raise the building after we get the logs ready."

"I'll tell my stepfather I can't stay long. Do you think he'll be angry, Aunt Rachel?"

"Of course not!" said Uncle Richard. "Henry Sparrow is a fine man. He'll be glad you have a chance to go to school."

However, Mr. Sparrow didn't act glad when he was told on Sunday. "Your mother won't like a short visit, Nancy," he said. "She's expecting you to live with us."

Nancy was surprised, and so were her aunt and uncle. The boys were so upset they didn't know what to do.

"Do you mean live there for—for good?" Nancy asked in a trembling voice.

"We want you. We've wanted you for a long time. There's no danger now from Indians."

"Will there be a school near your farm?" Mrs. Berry asked.

"Not for some time, Rachel. There aren't enough people in our neighborhood."

"Why don't you and Lucy let Nancy stay here and go to school?" Mr. Berry asked.

"We want her here, Henry," Mrs. Berry said. "She's one of our family. We couldn't get along without her, could we, boys?"

"I couldn't," Frank replied.

"Neither could I," Ned said.

138

"Well," began Mr. Sparrow slowly, "her mother is anxious for Nancy to get some learning. I have an idea she'll let her come back."

Then he smiled at his stepdaughter. "Just don't take all your clothes, honey. One other dress will be enough."

Everyone smiled and thought Henry Sparrow was a fine man, a mighty fine man.

The week that followed was a long one for the Berry family. They were all worried. They were afraid that Nancy wouldn't come back. Rosie, Luke, and Sammie were afraid of this, too. They were talking about it one night in their cabin.

"It's mighty quiet up in the big cabin now," Rosie said. "Mr. and Mrs. Berry and the boys just can't get along without that little girl."

"She had a nice disposition," Luke said. "She never quarreled with the boys or got mad at them when they teased her."

"It's no wonder they all love her," Rosie added. "I love her myself."

"So do I," Sammie said. "She was good to me. She taught me how to say my A B C's. Isn't she coming back here to live?"

"We don't know," his father answered. "We ought to know pretty soon, though."

140

"We'll just have to wait and see," said his mother. "Nobody knows."

Mr. Berry and his sons had another worry, too. It had rained every day for almost a week. Now the ground was so wet that it was impossible for anyone to work in the forest. Not one tree had been felled, and not one log was ready for the new school.

At last the rain stopped and the sun came out. Mr. Berry and the boys began to chop. Four men who lived near by came to help them.

The next day Nancy came home. Her stepfather brought her. He said it was pretty hard on Lucy to give Nancy up, but she was willing to do it anyway. She knew Nancy was smart and ought to have a chance to learn. There was little chance of a school being built in her community soon, so she was sending Nancy back.

"We think Nancy's smart, too, Henry," said Mrs. Berry.

"Yes, indeed," said Mr. Berry. "We all think so. Don't we boys?"

Frank and Ned nodded their heads.

"I've been thinking the same thing myself this last week," Henry said.

Nancy blushed and hurried out to see Rosie. She wasn't used to having people talk about her that way and she was embarrassed.

Short and Long Stitches

THE FOLLOWING week Mrs. Berry had a "quilting." She invited the wives of the four neighbors who were working with Mr. Berry. Their young daughters were invited, too, for they were Nancy's friends.

The ladies wasted no time after they arrived. They drew stools up to the quilting frame. They threaded needles and put on thimbles. Then they began to quilt.

Their daughters weren't allowed to be idle. They were to have a sewing lesson, along with Nancy. They were sitting on benches near the quilting frames, and each girl was sewing.

They weren't making anything. They were just sewing scraps of linen together in seams.

Now Mrs. Guffy left her work and examined the seams. "Your stitches are too long, girls. Your seam will pull apart."

A little later Mrs. Cross said the same thing.

Fifteen minutes after that Mrs. Paddock said even worse. "My goodness! You'll catch your fingernails in those long stitches."

Mrs. Berry shook her head when she looked. "You'd catch your toenails in them if it was a hem on a sheet."

The girls laughed and tried hard to make shorter stitches. The women went on quilting and talking.

"Girls," said Mrs. Cross, "did you ever hear about my grandmother? She wouldn't sleep under a cover quilted with long stitches. She was afraid she'd get caught in them and couldn't get out of bed if the cabin was on fire."

144

"I heard she took her own quilt when she went visiting," Mrs. Guffy added.

"Is it true?" Nancy asked.

"Well, that's the story I heard," Mrs. Cross replied. "I guess it is."

Now Mrs. Long told a story about a girl in her settlement. "She wore pretty dresses and she made them herself. So the boys thought she would make a good wife.

"One night she wore a new dress to a corn-husking. It was pink linen. She looked so pretty in it all the boys wanted to dance with her. They didn't know about the long stitches in the hem of her skirt.

"Well, she started to dance with her partner and what do you think happened?"

"What?" asked the girls.

"The young man caught his spur in the long stitches of the hem," said Mrs. Long. "He fell and broke his leg."

The girls were suspicious. They wanted to know if it was a true story.

"You'd think it's true when I tell you how it ended. Not one of those boys would marry her. They said her stitches were too long."

The girls giggled and said, "Oh my! Oh dear! Dear me!" But they tried hard to take still shorter stitches.

After dinner Mrs. Paddock told the story about the new settler and his hunting shirt.

"His wife was lazy," she began. "She would not bother to make a good strong shirt with short stitches. 'What's the use?' she said to herself. 'Nobody sees a hunting shirt but wolves, bears, deer and the like.'

"So she just galloped along with her stitches and the shirt was finished in no time. The settler put it on and went into the forest to hunt.

"He was looking about for a deer when he saw an Indian hunter through the trees. Quickly he hid in some thick bushes. Then a queer thing happened. The Indian hid in some bushes close by.

" 'He's hiding from some enemy,' the settler thought. 'Maybe several enemies from another tribe. They might find me before they find him. I'll creep out of this trap right now.'

"But he couldn't move. Twigs had caught in the long stitches in his shirt hem. They were caught in the shoulder seams and around both sleeves. He'd have to break the twigs to get loose from the bushes.

"He didn't dare to do this. The brave would hear the twigs snapping. Then he saw something moving. He parted the branches to see better.

"A large snake was crawling toward him!"

"Oh! Oh!" shrieked the girls.

"The poor man didn't know what to do. There was the Indian! Here was the snake! He was so frightened his heart almost stopped beating.

148

"Then he saw a young Indian boy coming with a bow. The next instant an arrow killed the snake. The brave left his hiding place. He smiled at the boy and patted his head fondly as they went away.

"Now twigs snapped and cracked and cracked and snapped. At last the settler was free, but his shirt was torn to pieces.

"He went straight home. And then he certainly taught his lazy wife how to sew."

"How did he teach her, Mother?" Ella asked.

"I promised I wouldn't tell."

Everyone laughed. Then everyone stopped talking. The women quilted and the girls sewed on their practice seams.

No one complained about the girls' stitches now. Mrs. Berry said they were so short she could hardly see them.

This pleased the girls and made their mothers very proud of them. When the party was over, everyone went home happy. The girls had learned something, and their mothers had enjoyed the quilting and the talking, especially the talking.

Then Mrs. Berry told Rosie something she hadn't said to the company. "Nancy's seams were the straightest and the neatest. She can sew better than any girl of her age I ever saw."

Quick to Learn
and Act

Rosie was pleased. "I declare, Mrs. Berry, I never heard of anybody learning so fast as Miss Nancy."

Mrs. Berry was pleased also. "I never did either, Rosie. And she's only eleven and one half, too."

"Six months ago she was just sewing up seams. Now she's made this pretty dress for herself," Rosie went on.

"She's helping her girl cousins and friends with their sewing now. Mrs. Paddock asked her to help Ella today."

Rosie nodded. "I saw her walking that way.

But not one of the girls learned their sewing lessons the way Miss Nancy did."

"She should have been in school all this time learning other lessons. Mr. Berry and I are disappointed about that."

"It wasn't your fault the teacher got the ague and couldn't come. The schoolhouse was ready for him."

"We're looking for a traveling teacher now, but there hasn't been one in this neighborhood. So many schools have been started in Kentucky since the war ended. The teachers don't need to travel about."

"You'll be getting one here by and by."

"I hope it won't be long."

"If it is, Miss Nancy will be teaching him to read. Ha, ha!"

"She can read a little in her First Reader now," said Mrs. Berry proudly.

"I know she can and I'm proud of her myself,"

said Rosie. "So are Luke and Sammie. Sammie thinks she's just about the smartest thing there is. She's taught him some of his A B C's, you know. He's mighty proud of that."

"Don't wait supper for her, Rosie. She's always late when she goes to see Ella."

So the family was eating when Nancy came. "I'm sorry I'm late," she said. "But I couldn't get away. The sheriff was there."

"The sheriff! Why was he there?" her uncle asked, surprised.

"He wanted to ask about the Adams family. Their farm is near Mr. Paddock's, you know."

Mr. Berry nodded. "Yes, and I know Mr. Adams. He's a good man. I hope he isn't in any kind of trouble."

"I guess he is, but it's on account of his son Roy," Nancy said. "He's the one the Indians sent back, you know."

"Oh," exclaimed Ned, "I know all about him!

The Indians captured him when he was a baby. He's my age now—he's fifteen."

"I saw him not long ago," said Frank, "and, he still looked like an Indian. He'd been home six months, but his hair was long and braided."

"It will be hard for him to be like a white boy," said Mrs. Berry. "He's lived with Indians all his life until now."

"It wasn't because they didn't want him that they sent him back," said Mr. Berry. "General Wayne made every tribe agree to return their captives."

Nancy had been waiting for a chance to speak. She had big news to tell. Now there was a pause. "He ran away last night!" she cried.

"Ran away!" exclaimed the boys.

"Ran away!" exclaimed their mother. "Where would he go?"

"Back to the Indians, you may be sure," Mr. Berry replied. "Many captives have run away

from their white relatives. Every one of them declared they loved their Indian families and
friends more than their own families."

"The boy's father tried to track him," Nancy
now went on. "He hunted for him all day, but
he couldn't find him. So the sheriff is going to
look tomorrow."

"Why don't they let the boy go back to his
Indian parents?" asked Frank.

"That's against the law," his father replied.
"The sheriff is compelled to hunt him."

"He asked Mr. Paddock all about Roy," said
Nancy. "He wanted to know how his folks
treated him."

"I'd say they were good to him."

"Their neighbors said they were, Uncle Richard. Roy wouldn't help his father with the farm
work, either. He said the land belonged to the
Indians and the whites had no right to cut down
their trees and plow the soil."

"He's got to learn," Frank put in.

"He wouldn't wear the suit his mother made for him," Nancy went on. "And he wouldn't wear the shoes his father made."

Ned said, "I suppose he wanted to wear his Indian clothes and moccasins."

"Yes, Ned, he did, and he wore them, too. His sister said he wouldn't sleep in a bed. He rolled up in a blanket and slept on the floor. She said they almost had a fight over his hair. When his father started to cut it, Roy pulled a long knife from his belt."

"Goodness gracious!" exclaimed Mrs. Berry. "I'd be afraid of that boy."

"They were, after that. Susie said they didn't say another word about his braids."

"I should think not!" Mrs. Berry exclaimed.

"Just wait till you hear what he did when he ran away! You'll all be scared. He took his father's gun!"

"That's bad," said her uncle. "The boy is so upset he's dangerous. He's likely to shoot anyone who tries to take him back."

"That's what the sheriff said. But I feel sorry for him."

"Sorry!" exclaimed Frank. "I think he needed a good licking."

"No! No!" cried Nancy. "He couldn't help what he did. He was homesick!"

"Homesick for a dirty Indian village and tepee!" Frank cried.

"Maybe his tribe kept things clean. And maybe it was in a pretty place," Nancy said.

"Maybe. Ha!"

"Anyway, he loved his Indian parents and his Indian brothers and sisters," said Nancy. "And he just had to be with them again. That's the way I felt about all of you when I went away."

"Hush, Nancy!" Frank cried. "You're making me feel sorry for Roy."

"I pity the poor boy," Mr. Berry said. "I almost hope they won't find him."

"I agree with you, Richard," said his wife. Then she reminded him that the blackberries were ripe and wondered when they should plan to go and pick some.

"Let Nancy and Ned go," Mr. Berry said. "They can go tomorrow if you want them to."

CAN NANCY GET THE GUN?

The next morning Nancy and Ned had an early breakfast. They had finished by daylight. Soon afterward they started for the blackberry patch. Each of them carried a large bucket.

They were bound for a large patch on a nearby hillside. It was a long walk, but they didn't mind. They were both strong and they liked to walk through the woods.

"I hope the berries haven't all been picked,"

said Nancy. They were in sight of the patch now and she began to worry.

"There's someone!" said Ned. "I see his head over those bushes."

"He pointed and Nancy looked. "Oh! It's Tom Lincoln!" she cried. "I know his black hair."

"Hello, Tom!" called Ned.

Tom came out of the patch smiling. He was a tall handsome boy of sixteen or so. "I beat you here," he said. "But I hadn't begun to pick."

"Your bucket shows that and so do your teeth," Ned said.

Nancy and Tom laughed. Then Tom said he was ready to begin if they were. "But we can't stay together. We can get more berries if we spread out. If you need help, Nancy, just hoot."

"Why would I need help?"

"Oh, you might see a little snake or a big bear."

"I'll hoot if I do."

Then they began to pick berries and there was

no more talk. Before long the pickers were far apart. Nancy stripped bush after bush. Her bucket was almost full now and she began to wonder if Ned and Tom were ready to go.

"I can't hoot," she thought. "They'd think I was in trouble."

Suddenly she heard a noise she didn't understand. At once she froze, just as her uncle had taught her to do. She didn't even move a hand or a foot.

Now she heard the noise again. This time she knew what it was. Someone was groaning. It might be someone from the settlement.

But she didn't rush from the bushes to find out. Her uncle had taught her this also. "There has always been danger in the wilderness," he had said. "Be careful at all times, and don't rush into trouble."

She parted the branches carefully and looked out. She was surprised by what she saw. The

160

berry patch ended here. Beyond it were great rocks clear to the top of the hill.

Now she heard the groan again, almost at her feet. A boy was lying over there by a rock. He was an Indian boy! His dark hair was long and braided. "Why," she thought, "it's the captive boy! It's Roy Adams!"

A gun was on the ground—his father's gun, of course, Nancy thought. Then she remembered her uncle's words yesterday: "The boy is so upset he's dangerous."

Nancy knew Roy needed help, but she didn't dare go to him. "He might be able to lift his gun and shoot," she said to herself. "He'd aim at this bush if he heard a noise here. And if I call and Tom and Ned come, he might shoot one of them, too."

Roy was moaning now and Nancy knew he was in pain. She knew he should be taken home and be put to bed and cared for. "The boys

161

could carry him," she thought. "But he wouldn't let them come near him."

Well, there was only one way to help. She'd have to get his gun. "It's close to my bush," she said to herself. "I can reach out and take it."

There was one danger. His ears would be keen like an Indian's. He might hear branches move when she reached out. And he might get the gun before she could reach it.

But she was sure she wouldn't make any noise, and she decided to try it. She got down on her knees. Then slowly, slowly, she reached for the gun. Now she had it! She thrust it quietly beneath a bush.

There was a slight rustle of leaves. Nancy couldn't help that. It was so slight she didn't think Roy would hear, but he did. He sat up and reached for his gun!

Nancy wondered what he would do when he found it wasn't there. It was then she knew he was very sick. He fell back on the ground moaning. He made no further effort to get the gun.

She knew she had nothing to fear now. So she stood and give a signal. "Hoo-oo!" she called.

"Hoo-oo!" Ned answered.

"Hoo-oo!" Tom called.

In just a little time they came. With Ned were Mr. Adams, the sheriff, and his two men. They had seen Ned as they rode by the patch and had stopped to ask if he had seen Roy.

Nancy pointed to the boy lying close to a great rock. "He was there when I saw him."

"It's Roy!" cried Mr. Adams. He turned to his son's side.

The other men followed. The sheriff passed his hands over Roy's body gently. When he touched the boy's right leg, Roy groaned.

"It's broken in two places," the sheriff said. "I suppose he jumped from this rock and fell. He's hurt bad. We'll have to hold him on a horse if we can. It will be quite a job getting him back home even after we set his leg."

"I'll walk and hold him on one side," Tom Lincoln offered.

"I'll walk on the other side," Ned offered.

"Thanks, boys," said the sheriff. "But my men here are used to that kind of thing."

"Yes, indeed!" agreed one. "You boys go on and pick your berries."

Now Nancy remembered the gun. She took it from the bush and gave it to Mr. Adams. Then, of course, she had to explain how she got it.

"You're a brave girl," Mr. Adams said. "I thank you for myself and his mother."

"Your son will thank her too," said the sheriff. "He'll get used to white people by the time he's well and be grateful for your love and care." Then he turned to Nancy. "I'm proud of you, little girl, proud of your courage and kindness.

"Now, men, let's lift the boy gently."

In the Cave

Mr. Berry had sold some horses to a settler in the cave county. But he hadn't been paid, so he decided to go for his money. He said the family could go along if they wanted to.

"I've always wanted to go there," said Mrs. Berry. "I've heard that Hart County is full of caves. Is that true?"

"There are a good many. Some of them have never been entered. But I do know about the largest cave down there. I've been in it and that's where I'll take you. It's called Big Cave."

Yes, indeed, they all knew, and they were all anxious to see it. So one morning they ate breakfast by candlelight. At sunrise they were ready to go.

The boys laughed at the things their mother had put in the wagon. "Here's medicine for snake bites and poison ivy," said Frank. "Here's some more for fever and chills."

"You never can tell what will happen on a trip," Mrs. Berry said. "We're going into rough country you know."

"But we're to be gone only one day," said Ned. "We won't need quilts."

"Someone might get sick. I just brought four, and two bearskin rugs."

"Ha, ha!" shouted the boys. "Ha, ha, ha!"

"It isn't funny," their father said. "Your mother knows what she's doing. She has lived in the wilderness longer than you."

Luke was to drive the team of strong horses. Mr. Berry and Frank were also on the driver's seat. Mrs. Berry was comfortable in her rocker.

Nancy and Ned sat on the bearskin rugs at the rear end.

Rosie and Sammie were on a bench with the dinner basket between them. Rosie held the basket firmly. "I don't want this food jolted out and rolled all over the floor," she explained. "And I don't want Sammie rolling with it." So she held onto him, too.

Nancy watched birds. Ned watched squirrels. Sometimes they sang just because they were happy. When Frank started "The Horse Cave Gallop," they sang with him.

"Look!" Nancy cried suddenly. "There! Wild turkeys! In that old oak tree!" Then she began to sing "The Turkey Gobbler." The others sang the chorus.

They were all so happy they had to sing. No hard work today. Nothing but fun—pure fun. So they made the forest ring with their "Gobble, gobble, gobble."

168

"I hate to brag," said Jonathan Lee,
"But no one can tell a turkey from me.

"I can gobble like her and gobble like he,
When I creep to their roost in the old
beech tree."

Gobble, gobble, gobble,
Gobble, gobble, gobble.
Gobble!

When Jonathan Lee went out to tea,
He tried to act like a wild turkee.
He danced, he pranced, he flipped a
wing,
It was funny to see, it was, by jing!

Then out one day in the early dawn,
On, on, he crept. On, on and on.
And before he reached the old beech tree,
He began to gobble like a wild turkee.

But the wary birds rose up and flew,
'Twas no gobbler of theirs, they very
well knew.
But just for fun they showed young Lee
The right way to gobble to a wild turkee.

Now everyone tried to give the wild turkey call but they couldn't. So they just screeched instead, and laughed.

They stopped around ten o'clock to rest the horses. They decided to eat their lunch now—they were all hungry. Then on to Big Cave!

"Here we are!" cried Mr. Berry at last. "There's the opening to the cave in the hillside. We'll get our torches ready at once."

The boys built a fire while their father and Luke cut off tree branches. These were trimmed. Then one end of each branch was held in the fire until it was blazing.

Now they followed Mr. Berry into the cave, one by one. They all had to stoop and lower their torches, even Sammie. They went down some stepping stones into inky blackness and cold damp air.

"This is scary," said Nancy. "I'm afraid, Uncle Richard."

170

"There's nothing to be afraid of," said her uncle. "Now then, look!"

"Oh!" cried the others, astonished. "Oh! Oh!"

BRAVE LITTLE NANCY HANKS

Inside the cave they saw a large room with white stone walls. They saw great stone ferns and flowers.

"The flowers and ferns look real," said Mrs. Berry. "You'd think they were made by men."

"They were all made by water dripping from the roof of the cave," Mr. Berry explained.

"I don't see how water could make these big ferns," said Ned.

"Do you see how it could make that angel up there on that wall?" Frank asked. "And look at that pulpit! It's all ready for the preacher."

"Just think of water making that angel's wings!" said Rosie.

171

"Can the angel fly with them?" Sammie asked his mother.

"Of course not! They're stone—she's stone. She's got to stay here forever."

"We'll explain about all these things on the way home," said Mr. Berry. "It's a long story about the dripping water in caves."

Mr. Berry now crossed to an opening and held his torch high. "Here's the river!" he cried. "Follow me."

The others followed him into a narrow dark passage. The torches showed them the flowing black water. Nancy took hold of her uncle's hand. "It's pretty," she said, "but I'd hate to fall into it."

"Be careful or you will," Frank warned. "Don't go to the edge of the bank, Ned. It's slippery and you might slip."

"I was just going to dip my hand into the water. I wanted to see how cold it is."

"Don't go a step closer," said his father. "Hunters have told me about this river. It's icy cold and dangerous."

"And don't try to swim in it," his brother joked. "You're likely to freeze to death."

"A hunter told me there were blind fish in this river," said Luke.

"I want to see blind fish!" Sammie cried.

"Never mind them. And stay away from the river. Come back here!"

"I never did see a blind fish."

"They'll jump out of the water pretty soon," Frank joked. "They'll want to see who's here."

The others laughed—all except Sammie. He didn't get the joke.

"I can't understand about the river," Nancy said. "How did it get down here under the ground, Uncle Richard?"

"I'll tell you on the way home. That's also a long story."

"Let's go!" exclaimed Mrs. Berry. "It's cold in here."

As the others followed they left their torches between stone flowers and ferns. While they were doing this Nancy went back to the river.

She wanted to look at the black water again. No one saw her go except Sammie, and he didn't stop to tell anyone. He just followed her.

Nancy was surprised when Sammie spoke to her. She could see him because a torch had been left there.

"I wanted to see the blind fish come up," he said. Then he forgot and went too close to the slippery edge. His foot slipped and the next instant he was in the river.

"Swim!" Nancy cried. "I'll call the men. They'll get you out! Swim, Sammie! Swim!" She knew he could. She had seen him swimming in Beech River. She had learned to swim in the river herself.

174

The boy made a few feeble motions and stopped. Nancy knew then that he was too frightened to swim.

"Help! Help!" she shouted. Then she jumped into the river to save him. She grabbed him just as he began to sink.

She held him up with one arm and swam about with the other. All the time she was screaming for help, but no one came.

The water was so cold she was growing numb. She couldn't hold Sammie up much longer. She couldn't swim much longer. She tried to call again, but her voice was weak. She knew they wouldn't hear her.

"They'll miss us," she thought, "and they'll come here." But she couldn't last much longer. She was so weak—so weak—so——

"Nancy!" called her uncle from the front of the cave. "Are you in here?"

"Sammie! Where are you?" Luke cried.

"Help! Help!"

It was a weak little voice but they heard it. In a moment Mr. Berry and Luke were pulling the children from the river.

The ride home was a quiet one. If anyone spoke, he spoke softly. Nancy and Sammie were asleep. They were both snug and warm with bearskins under them and clean quilts over them.

"Are you sure they're all right, Rachel?" Mr. Berry asked softly.

"Yes, indeed! They weren't in the water long —not more than two or three minutes. I'll give them another dose of medicine as soon as they wake up."

"I'm sorry I laughed about the quilts and medicine, Mother," Frank whispered.

"So am I," whispered Ned.

Mrs. Berry patted each boy's hand. Now there was silence for a time. Then Rosie spoke to Mrs. Berry softly. "That little girl risked her life to save my boy. Think of her jumping into that black water!"

"It took great courage."

"It took a lot of feeling in her heart, Mrs. Berry," Rosie went on. "I reckon she'll always forget herself if she can help somebody else in some way."

The Frontier Wedding

June 12, 1806, was a lovely day in Kentucky. Roses were in full bloom. They hung in clusters on bushes around the Berry cabin in Beechland. They climbed over its log walls and made it a fairy bower.

Inside, the cabin was sweet with their fragrance. Red roses were in large gourds hanging on the walls. Pink and white roses were in smaller gourds on the long mantelshelf.

"It's pretty," Nancy Hanks said as she looked about the large room. "It smells sweet, too."

"It's a fine day for your wedding," Frank Berry said. "I'm sure all of our kin will come."

"I think all of Tom's kin are coming," Nancy said happily. "I'm so glad! I hope his mother can get here. The creeks are a little high now."

"If she's anything like Tom she won't be afraid of high water. He'd roll up his coattails and cross over. And she'll roll up her skirts."

Nancy nodded and smiled proudly. "I never knew him to run away from any hardship, Frank, in all the years I've known him."

"He never will. He's a fine young man. I'm glad you're going to marry him. You two grew up here in this county."

"We picked blackberries together," Nancy added. "That was when I was twelve and he was only sixteen."

Now Frank's wife Elizabeth came into the room. "You'd better dress right away, Nancy," she advised. "You don't have much time."

"But the wedding isn't till noon! And we've just finished breakfast."

"The relatives will come early. They always do at weddings," Elizabeth replied.

Nancy turned to go, then she stopped and spoke to Frank. "I wish Aunt Rachel and Uncle Richard might have lived to see this day."

"So do I, Nancy. Your marriage would have made them happy."

Then Nancy went into a small room with Elizabeth to put on her bridal dress.

Soon afterwards the guests began to arrive. They dismounted from their horses at the stile block. Turned-up skirts and coattails were turned down. Hair was smoothed and spurs were removed.

Guests from near-by Beechland and Springfield hitched their own horses. They were careful about this. They tied the horses to a swinging beech limb every time.

"You've got to give your animal a chance to fight flies," one man explained. Everyone understood what he meant, for all Kentuckians loved horses.

Guests who came from a distance were met by Luke and Sammie. Their horses were unsaddled and turned into the pasture. Kentucky horses must be treated right.

"It's going to be a big wedding," Sammie said as he and his father were coming back to the stile block. "It looks as if everyone in the county is here already."

"There are more to come from other counties," his father replied. "There's a heap of kin on both sides of the family—the Lincoln side and the Hanks side. They've got a heap of friends, too, you know."

"I just took the judge's horse, Pappy," said Sammie. "He told me he couldn't hold court today in Springfield."

"Of course he couldn't. The lawyers are all kin and are coming to the wedding. So he just ups and comes himself. But he was invited by Mr. Tom Lincoln."

"Nobody's supposed to come unless invited. Mr. Ned Berry said for me to call him if anyone tried to push in."

"They'll be trying," Luke declared. "They want to eat the fine dinner—they can smell it a mile away. They know that kettles are boiling, ovens baking, venison frying, and sheep roasting. And Rosie is bossing it all."

The men guests stayed in the yard and talked about their crops and horses. The women went into the cabin, and of course they talked about Nancy's wedding dress.

Nancy was still in her room getting ready, but several relatives and friends had seen her wedding dress.

"She made it herself," said an aunt, "so you know it will be well made."

"Indeed it will," another aunt agreed. "Nancy

183

sews beautifully. She's the best seamstress in Washington County."

"She's better than anyone in Mercer County," said Mrs. Henry Sparrow. "I'm proud of her."

"You have a right to be, Lucy," another aunt declared. "She made my daughter's wedding dress and it was beautiful."

"I'm sorry Nancy and Tom won't be living near by," Ella Paddock said. "I can't see her often if they live in Elizabethtown."

"We're all sorry about that," said Frank Berry's wife. "Tom owns a house there. He has a little farm there, too."

"And he's a good carpenter," one of the Lincolns told them. "He'll be able to take care of Nancy. You needn't worry about her."

"S-sh!" a lady whispered. "The preacher is coming! He's getting off his horse. Luke is taking it. He's coming through the gate."

The ladies straightened their dresses and

184

smoothed their hair. Then the Reverend Jesse Head entered the cabin. The men followed him, and with them was handsome young Thomas Lincoln, the groom.

He crossed to the fireplace and stood in front of it. The preacher joined him at once.

Then came the bride, looking tall and slender, in her wedding dress. It was a beautifully made white linen and she looked lovely in it.

The clock struck twelve as Nancy Hanks crossed the room and stood by the groom's side, facing the minister.

Presently the ceremony was over and Miss Nancy Hanks was Mrs. Thomas Lincoln.

The wedding dinner followed. It was really a feast and something to be remembered. And it was remembered. Twenty years later, the Reverend Jesse Head told a newspaper reporter about the food.

"A sheep had been roasted whole," he said.

"It was delicious. There was also bear meat, venison, wild turkey, duck, vegetables and eggs, both wild and tame."

The reporter smiled. "Tame eggs?" he asked.

"Chickens weren't common then," Mr. Head explained. "Too many varmints to kill them."

"Oh, I see. So tame eggs were really a treat."

"They were, sir. There was another treat, too. This was maple sugar swinging on strings. It was nice to nibble on, that night."

"Did the wedding last till night?"

"It lasted all night and till the next morning after breakfast. The fiddlers took turns playing for the dancing. It nearly wore them out because the Virginia Reel and square sets were going till the sun came up the next morning."

"Did the bride and groom dance all night?"

"No, I don't think they did. They slipped away somehow and mounted their horses and rode off."

"Where did they go?" asked the reporter.

"I don't know," said Mr. Head. "Maybe to Tom's house in Elizabethtown. Or maybe to visit relatives for a day or two. But I can tell you this much—they'd be welcome wherever they went. Nobody in the county was thought more highly of than Nancy and Tom Lincoln."

In Memoriam

MANY YEARS later a large group of Girl Scouts left their bus in Lincoln State Park in southern Indiana. They followed their leader quietly to a beautiful shrine.

As they gazed at the shrine their leader spoke softly. "The State of Indiana erected this building in honor of one of our great presidents, Abraham Lincoln," she said, "and also in honor of his mother, Nancy Hanks Lincoln."

Jeanette was puzzled. "Why was the shrine built here in Spencer County?" she asked.

"The Lincolns moved here from Kentucky," the Scout leader answered. "This land was part of their farm. Abraham grew up here and his mother was buried here."

"She must have been proud of her son," Beatrice said.

"She died when he was just a boy—he was only nine," said the leader. "But his father lived to see him elected to Congress."

"I wish his mother could have known that," Helen said softly.

The other girls nodded and showed their regret in their young faces.

Presently a group of women and men stood in the place the girls had just left.

"Just think of it!" one lady exclaimed. "Nancy Hanks, a girl of the Kentucky backwoods—the mother of one of the greatest men the world has ever known."

"Yes," another lady agreed. "Pretty Nancy Hanks, who married Tom Lincoln, a neighbor boy in the Beechland settlement in Kentucky."

"Neither of them had much education," a third lady said.

"They lived before the days of books and schools for poor people, but they weren't ignorant," her husband interrupted. "They knew how to make a living in the wilderness. And that was an important thing then."

"I agree with you," said another man. "President Lincoln once told a friend that his mother had a fine mind."

"He must have been thinking of her refinement and her love for all that was good and honest in life," a lady added.

"I suppose so. He said she was a real lady."

"I like to think of the qualities President Lincoln inherited from his mother," a lady remarked. "He said that she was gentle and kind, and that she had great pity for all who suffered. Couldn't we say that about him, too?"

"We could indeed!" a man exclaimed. "No

man had more pity for those who suffered. He freed the Negro slaves because of this. And because of it his memory is revered by the poor and downtrodden of all lands."

"The girl Nancy was loved dearly by the relatives with whom she lived in Kentucky," another lady stated. "They said she was unselfish and kind and gentle always."

"Her neighbors here in Indiana were fond of her," another women added. "They said she was ever a true friend to them."

Now a minister spoke. "This shrine is a lovely reminder of that lovely woman, so tender and gentle and so true of heart.

"It is also a reminder of her wonderful son, the true friend of all mankind."

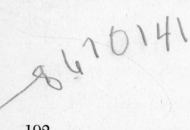

More About This Book

WHEN NANCY HANKS LIVED

1784   NANCY HANKS WAS BORN IN VIRGINIA.

The country consisted of thirteen colonies joined under the Articles of Confederation.

The country was governed by Congress and four department ministers.

The population of the country was about 3,240,000.

1788   NANCY MOVED TO KENTUCKY WITH HER FAMILY.

George Washington became the first President, 1789.

The first session of Congress was held, 1789.

1790   NANCY LIVED WITH HER AUNT AND UNCLE AFTER HER MOTHER REMARRIED.

The first census was taken, 1790.

A banking system was established in the United States, 1791.

Kentucky became a state, 1792.

Eli Whitney invented the cotton gin, 1793.

John Adams was President, 1797-1801.

1801   NANCY HANKS MARRIED THOMAS LINCOLN.

Thomas Jefferson was President, 1801-1809.

The United States bought the Louisiana Territory, 1803.

Lewis and Clark explored the Northwest Territory, 1804-1806.

Zebulon Pike explored the area now known as Kansas, Colorado, and New Mexico, 1806.

Robert Fulton built the "Clermont," the first practical steamboat, 1807.

1809   NANCY'S SON, ABRAHAM LINCOLN, WAS BORN NEAR HODGENVILLE, KENTUCKY.

The War of 1812 was fought, 1812-1815.

"The Star-Spangled Banner" was written, 1814.

First account of the Lewis and Clark Expedition was published, 1814.

General Andrew Jackson defeated a British army at the Battle of New Orleans, 1815.

1816   THOMAS AND NANCY LINCOLN MOVED TO INDIANA.

Indiana became a state, 1816.

Construction of the Erie Canal was begun, 1817.

194

1818   NANCY HANKS LINCOLN DIED IN OCTOBER.

There were twenty states in the Union.

James Monroe was President.

The population of the country was about
9,150,000.

DO YOU REMEMBER?

1. In what state was Nancy Hanks born?

2. How old was Nancy when she moved to Kentucky?

3. How did Nancy's family travel on the way to Kentucky?

4. What did Nancy do one day that frightened a family of newcomers near her new home in Kentucky?

5. Who was Patrick Murphy and why was Nancy glad when he came to the Berry farm?

6. What did Nancy discover about Patrick Murphy one day when she went to hunt her dog?

7. How did Nancy get to keep the primer which the Dix family left behind?

8. Why were Mr. Berry and his neighbors worried about the Cumberland Indians in 1792?

9. Where did the county militia hold its drill?

10. What was the "silver gang" trying to do?

11. How did the silver gang plan to force Mr. Berry's militia company to help them?

12. What happened to the silver gang?

13. Which of Nancy's relatives fought under General Anthony Wayne against the Indians?

14. Why did Nancy's mother and stepfather decide to let Nancy go on living with the Berrys?

15. What did Nancy and her friends do while their mothers were busy at the quilting?

16. How did Nancy help Roy Adams?

17. Where was the stream into which Sammie fell?

18. Whom did Nancy marry, and when?

IT'S FUN TO LOOK UP THESE THINGS

1. What kind of supplies would a pioneer family moving to Kentucky take with them?

2. What was the county militia of which Richard Berry was captain?

3. What famous battle did General Anthony Wayne and his men fight against the Indians?

196

4. What famous cave is located near the place where Nancy Hanks lived in Kentucky?

5. What other kinds of parties did pioneers have besides quiltings?

6. Where were Nancy and Thomas Lincoln living when their son Abraham was born?

INTERESTING THINGS YOU CAN DO

1. Draw and color a picture of a pioneer home in Kentucky, showing the cabin, the clearing around it, the fields, and some of the forest beyond.

2. Prepare a short talk about Kentucky in pioneer times, telling what the country was like and how the pioneers lived and traveled. Be ready to give your talk to the class.

3. Learn some old songs or games that were popular in pioneer days and teach the class how to sing or play them. You may find such songs or games in books on pioneer life.

4. Form a committee to build a model frontier settlement out of cardboard. Make a fort and near by in the forest a settler's cabin with cleared fields.

OTHER BOOKS YOU MAY ENJOY READING

Abe Lincoln: Frontier Boy, Augusta Stevenson. Trade and School Editions, Bobbs-Merrill.

Abraham Lincoln: An Initial Biography, Genevieve Foster. Scribner.

Abraham Lincoln: Friend of the People, Clara Ingram Judson. Follett.

America's Abraham Lincoln, May McNeer. Houghton.

Buffalo Trace, Virginia S. Eifert. Dodd.

Nancy Hanks Lincoln of Wilderness Road, Meridel LeSueur. Knopf.

INTERESTING WORDS IN THIS BOOK

ague (ā′gū) : kind of illness accompanied by chills and fever

backwoods (băck′wŏŏdz′) : heavily forested lands far from thickly settled regions

complained (kŏm plānd′) : grumbled, expressed dissatisfaction

discouraged (dĭs kûr′ĭjd) : disheartened, made less eager and confident

disposition (dĭs′pó zĭsh′ŭn) : humor, state of mind

ferns: plants with numerous many-fingered leaves, often found in woods and gardens

fragrance (frā'grăns) : sweet smell

ford (fôrd) : shallow place where travelers may cross a river

gristmill: mill where grain is ground into meal or flour

hawk (hôk) : strong, swift bird that lives by catching other birds and small animals

hearth (härth) : brick or stone floor of a fireplace

johnnycakes: bread made from corn meal, eggs, milk, and flour

loom (lōōm) : machine for weaving cloth

loot (lōōt) : plunder, property taken from others by force, as during a war

militia (mĭ lĭsh'a) : number of citizens organized as a military group who serve actively as soldiers only in case of emergency

muzzle (mŭz''l) : the open end of a rifle barrel

posse (pŏs'ė) : band of armed men gathered to help enforce the law

qualities (kwŏl'ĭ tĭz) : traits that set something or someone apart from others

199

quicksand: seemingly solid mixture of sand and water into which a person can easily sink

quilting: act of making a quilt, a gathering or party at which people make quilts

ravine (rȧ vēn´) : kind of small valley made by running water

refinement (rė fīn´mĕnt) : state of being educated and well-mannered

revered (rė vērd´) : admired and respected greatly

shuck (shŭk) : remove the outer covering or shell as of corn or a nut

stile (stīl) : step or steps on each side of a fence by which people cross the fence

stockade (stŏk ād´) : wall formed by tall posts set on end and side by side

suspicious (sŭs pĭsh´ŭs) : doubtful, not trusting

tumblers (tŭm´blērz) : persons who perform acrobatic tricks

Virginia Reel: kind of dance once popular among pioneers and country people

volunteers (vŏl´ŭn tērz´) : persons who offer to do something of their own free will

yokes (yōks) : wooden bars or frames by which two oxen are hitched together, hence teams of oxen